TA

Specific Uniforms

© 2008 All Rights Reserved

Published by:

MENTOR ENTERPRISES, INC.

7910 Memorial Parkway SW, Suite F-1
Huntsville, Alabama 35802
info@MentorEnterprisesInc.com

for the purpose of this product, military regulations, local policies, and orders, are considered the governing sources concerning the subject matter. **Readers are encouraged to read all relevant material covering the subject involved**.

Every effort was made to ensure that this product was complete and accurate at the time of printing. *It is possible that mistakes may be found both in content and typography*. This product should be used only as a **guide** and not as the source or ultimate authority.

The purpose of the product is to educate and entertain only. The authors, agents, editors, or publisher shall have no liability or responsibility to any person or entity concerning loss/damage alleged, to be caused or caused by any means directly or indirectly by the information in this product.

By utilizing and purchasing this product the customer agrees and is in strict understanding and agreement that this product is provided without any expressed or implied warranties as to the products' completeness and/or correctness, legal effect, or validity.

This product should and can only be used as a guide (as previously stated). It should be modified to fit the situation that exists by seeking guidance from competent professionals including military lawyers, Inspector Generals, Equal Opportunity, proper staff agencies, or other competent staff professionals.

No warranty is made or implied with regard to the completeness, and/or correctness, legal effect, or validity, of this product in any state or jurisdiction. *It is further understood that any person or entity that utilizes this product does so at their own risk with full knowledge that they have a legal obligation, duty, and responsibility to ensure the information they provide is in accordance with up to date military law, procedure, regulation, policy, or order.* No part of this product shall in anyway substitute for professional guidance or expertise on a subject.

We encourage and welcome comments, suggestions, ideas, or questions at: info@mentorenterprisesinc.com

All material will be reviewed for possible use in future printings. Please provide your mailing address and phone number with your correspondence.

In this product the term "commander" refers to commanders at all levels. Some commanders have different types of authority. The local policy on the authority of a commander should be checked in your area. In addition, any reference to the term "he" should be understood to include both genders.

TERMS OF USE

By using this product you understand that this product is for **INDIVIDUAL USE ONLY.** In accordance with the non-exclusive license to use as described here in the non-exclusive license. It is understood and agreed that such duplication or copying in any medium, any resale or distribution to any other person or entity. It is specifically understood that there shall be no redrafting, republishing, or reengineering or in anyway use the material to create a similar derivative product, unless such product or derivative product is strictly for individual use of the person or entity who purchased the original license (product) to use.

Commanders' Authority and Individuals' Responsibilities, (Pg 6)

Commanders' Responsibilities, Table 1.1, (Pg 7)

To maintain uniformity and good order and discipline:

- **Major Command Commanders (see note 1)**
    - Supplement this instruction. Supplements must be approved by HQ AFPC/DPSO
    - Authorize wear of functional clothing with service uniforms
    - Authorize wear of civilian clothing on-duty and standardize clothing by activity (see note 2)
    - Prescribe wear of grade insignia, unit emblems, etc. on organizational or functional clothing
    - Determine acceptable off-base wear for all uniforms
    - Specify motorcycle and bicycle patrol uniforms for security forces personnel
    - Prescribe wear of "Personal Hydration System"
- **Installation Commanders**
    - Supplement this instruction. Further authorize specific guidance on wear of functional clothing with service uniforms that have previously been approved by MAJCOM Commander. Supplements must be approved by HQ AFPC/DPSO
    - Prohibit offensive civilian clothes and personal grooming based on legal, moral, safety, or sanitary grounds
    - Require protective or reflective items when safety considerations make it appropriate
    - Authorize Allowance Standard (AS) 016 approved organizational clothing and equipment

- o Process requests for approval of distinctive clothing items (see Chapter 7, Pg 156 for specific instructions)
- o Provide at no cost to enlisted members required organizational/functional items directed for wear.
- o Process requests for issue allowance organizational or functional according to AFMAN 23-110, Vol 2, USAF Supply Manual. Provide at no cost to officers optional items directed for wear
- o Prescribe wear of outergarments and accessories with security forces police uniforms. Process requests for issue allowance according to AFMAN 23-110, Vol 2, USAF Supply Manual
- o Prescribe wear of uniform during sporting events

- **Theater Commanders**
  - o Prescribe the dress and personal appearance standards in the theater of operations. Supplements are required. Coordinate supplements with HQ AFPC/DPSO prior to issuance

NOTES: **(Pg 8)**

1. For the purpose of this AFI, the National Guard Bureau is considered a MAJCOM.

2. All military personnel working in Services activities wear same type of clothing. Fitness Center Staff and Food Service personnel see Table 3.7 and Table 3.8. See Table 1.2 for guidance on civilian clothing allowance when required to wear civilian clothes to perform assigned duties.

Members identified as not presenting a professional military appearance (Pg 6)

- The Unit Commander:
  - o May require individuals who do not present a professional military appearance (regardless of overall fitness composite score) to enter the Fitness Improvement Program IAW AFI 10-248

   o Schedules individuals for Fitness
    Education/Intervention

Individuals' Responsibilities (Pg 6)

- To present a professional military image individual **will**:
  - o Procure and maintain all mandatory clothing items
  - o Review and follow local supplements and procedures
  - o Uniforms will be neat, clean, pressed, buttoned, and properly maintained
- Members **will not**
  - o Stand or walk with hands in pockets of any uniform combination, other than to insert or remove items
  - o Walk in uniform while using cell phones, radios, hands-free headsets unless required in the performance of official duties using a government issued device
  - o Smoke/use smokeless tobaccos, drink, or eat while walking in uniform

GENERAL MILITARY STANDARDS SECTION

Body/Physical Appearance Modification Standards, Table 2.5, (Pg 86)

Body Alteration or Modification, (Pg 86): Prohibited, if it is intentional and results in a visible, physical effect that detracts from a professional military image. Failure to observe these mandatory provisions and prohibitions by active duty Air Force members, USAFR members on active duty or inactive duty for training and ANG members in Federal service is a violation of Article 92, Uniform Code of Military Justice (UCMJ). (See note 1)

Body Piercing, (Pg 87): In Uniform: Members are prohibited from attaching, affixing or displaying objects, articles, jewelry, or ornamentation to or through the ear, nose, tongue, eye brows, lips, or any exposed body part (includes visible through the uniform). **EXCEPTION** : Women are authorized to wear earrings. (See Table 2.6) **Civilian Attire**: *(1) Official Duty*: Members are prohibited from attaching, affixing, or displaying objects, articles, jewelry, or ornamentation to or through the nose, tongue, eye brows, lips, or any exposed body part (includes visible through clothing).

(2) Off Duty on a military installation: Members are prohibited from attaching, affixing, or displaying objects, articles, jewelry, or ornamentation to or through the nose, tongue, eye brows, lips or any exposed body part (includes visible through clothing). Piercing of earlobes by women is allowed, but should not be extreme or excessive.

Tattoos/Brands, (Pgs 86-87)
          Unauthorized content. (Pg 86): Tattoos/brands anywhere on the body that are obscene or advocate sexual, racial, ethnic, or religious discrimination are prohibited in and out of uniform. Tattoos/brands that are prejudicial to good order and discipline or that are of a nature that tends to bring discredit upon the Air Force are prohibited in and out of uniform. Tattoos that are commonly associated with gang affiliations are prohibited both in and out of uniform. Unauthorized (content): Members who receive tattoos/brands not meeting the standards after the implementation of this policy are required to initiate tattoos/brands removal at their own expense upon notification by their commander. Initial accessions must disclose any tattoos and must complete removal of inappropriate tattoos prior to being accepted in the Air Force. Members failing to remove or alter unauthorized tattoos in a timely manner may be subject to disciplinary action or involuntary separation. Failure to observe these mandatory provisions and prohibitions by active duty Air Force members, USAFR members on active duty or inactive duty for training and ANG members in Federal service is a violation of Article 92, Uniform Code of Military Justice (UCMJ). *(See notes 2, 3, 4 and 5).*
          (Inappropriate-military image), (Pg 87) Excessive tattoos/brands will not be exposed or visible (includes visible through the uniform) while in uniform. Excessive is defined as any

8

tattoo/brands that exceed 1/4 of the exposed body part and those above the collarbone and readily visible when wearing an open collar uniform. Members should not be allowed to display excessive tattoos that would detract from an appropriate professional image while in uniform. Commanders should use these guidelines in determining appropriate military image and acceptability of tattoos displayed by members in uniform. Air Force members with tattoos not meeting an acceptable military image should be required to **(a)** maintain complete coverage of the tattoos using current uniform items (e.g., long-sleeved shirt/blouse, pants/slacks, dark hosiery, PT running suit, etc.) or **(b)** remove tattoo(s). Depending on the circumstances, commanders may seek Air Force medical support for voluntary tattoo removal. PTDY is not authorized in this situation and is at member's expense. Members failing to remove, cover, or alter excessive tattoos or who choose not to comply with acceptable military standards may be subject to disciplinary action or involuntary separation. Failure to observe these mandatory provisions and prohibitions by active duty Air Force members, USAFR members on active duty or inactive duty for training and ANG members in Federal service is a violation of Article 92, Uniform Code of Military Justice (UCMJ). **(See notes 2, 4, 5 and 6).**

NOTES: (Pg 88)

1. Members who intentionally alter or modify any part of their bodies in order to achieve a visible, physical effect that disfigures, deforms, or otherwise detracts from a professional military image may be subject to disciplinary action or involuntary separation, as determined appropriate by the member's commander. *Examples of prohibited conduct* include (but are not limited to) tongue splitting or forking, tooth filing, and acquiring visible, disfiguring skin implants.

2. Installation or *higher commanders may impose more restrictive standards* for tattoos and body ornaments, on or off duty, in those locations where Air Force-wide standards may not be adequate to address cultural sensitivities (e.g., overseas) or mission requirements (e.g., basic training environments).

9

3. Members who receive tattoos/brands not meeting the standards are required to initiate tattoos/brands removal at their own expense (may not use Air Force Medical Centers for removal) upon notification by their Commander. Members not complying with these requirements _will be_ subject to disciplinary action for failure to comply with Air Force Standards and may be involuntarily separated.

4. There may be situations where the commander can restrict the wear of non-visible body ornaments. Those situations would include any body ornamentation that interferes with the performance of the member's military duties. _The factors to be evaluated in making this determination include, but are not limited to:_ impairs the safe and effective operation of weapons, military equipment or machinery; poses a health or safety hazard to the wearer or others; or interferes with the proper wear of special or protective clothing or equipment (*EXAMPLE*: helmets, flack jackets, flight suits, camouflaged uniforms, gas masks, wet suits, and crash rescue equipment.)

5. Tattoo/branding policy went into effect 15 March 1998.

6. Members who receive tattoos/brands not meeting the standards after the implementation of this policy are required to initiate tattoos/brands removal at their own expense upon notification by their Commander. Members not complying with these requirements will be subject to disciplinary action for failure to comply with Air Force Standards and may be involuntarily separated.

Enlisted Personnel: Procure and maintain all mandatory clothing items listed in AFI 36-3014, *Clothing Allowances for Air Force Personnel*. Request a civilian clothing allowance in accordance with AFI 36-3014, when required to wear civilian clothes, for reasons such as safety or security, to perform assigned duties.

Officers: Procure and maintain all items necessary to meet standards of dress for assigned duties and mission requirements.

Officers and Enlisted Personnel:
- Purchase items from the Army Air Force Exchange Service (AAFES) Military Clothing Sales Stores (MCSS) supplied by the Defense Supply Center Philadelphia (DSCP) or commercial vendors.
- Purchase items from commercial vendors when items have a USAF certification label.
- Do not purchase uniform items from unauthorized manufacturers (note 3).

NOTES: **(Pg 8)**
1. Uniform clothing may be altered to improve fit. However, alterations must not change the intended appearance of garment as designed.
2. The omission of a specific item or appearance standard does not automatically permit its wear.
3. If it is not authorized; it is not authorized for wear.

Clothing/Accessory Standards. Table 2.6, (Pgs 89-91)

Athletic Shoes, (Pg 91) Medical waiver will only be approved by unit commander when recommended by appropriate medical authorities. Athletic shoes must be a conservative color (i.e., white, black, dark blue, gray, etc.) BDUs may be worn unbloused with athletic shoes.

Attaché case, gym bag, backpack, (Pg 91) Carried in left hand, on left shoulder, or both shoulders (not to interfere with rendering the proper salute). **Attaché case**: black only; **gym bags**: black or dark blue; **backpacks**: only solid-color black backpacks may be worn with blue uniform combinations; solid-color black, olive drab, or woodland camouflage are the only colors authorized with the BDU. Conservative manufacture's logo is allowed. Members may wear backpack using one or both shoulder straps. Allow small clutch or carry type with straps with mess dress. Small subdued logo (IAW sunglasses guidance). No ornamentation or design, nothing dangling. Color should be flat black, no high-gloss. Gold or silver clasps, no chains.

Bracelet _(1 only)_,(Pg 89) Conservative, no wider than 1/2 inch, and must not present safety hazard. Worn around the wrist. Ankle bracelets are not authorized. The wear of traditional metal POW/MIA bracelets, which come in colors beside silver, bronze, or gold, remains authorized. Conservative is defined as plain, not drawing attention, or faddish. (must be gold or silver). Bracelets for identification for medical alert purposes are authorized as long as they meet the standards above (conservative). Bracelets espousing support for a cause, philosophy, individual, or group are not authorized. Gemstones/tennis bracelets are authorized to be worn only with the mess dress uniform.

Clothing, (Pg 89) Neat, clean, pressed, proper fit, in good condition, zipped, snapped, or buttoned.

Common Access Card (CAC), (Pg 91) Allowed only to wear on base or when required. Will be worn on the front of the body, displayed above the waist and below the neck.

Earrings, _(Women)_ (Pg 89) Small, spherical, conservative, round diamond, gold, pearl, or silver earrings with any uniform combination and worn as a set. If member has multiple holes only one set of earrings will be worn in the lower earlobe. When members wear civilian clothes for duty they will conform to AFI requirements. Matching earrings must be worn and should fit tightly without extending below the earlobe. (*EXCEPTION:* Connecting band on clip earrings.)

Eyeglasses and Sunglasses, (Pg 90) Conservative ornamentation on frames and lenses. Authorize conservative ornamentation on non-prescription sunglasses or eyeglasses, frames may be black or brown material or gold or silver wire. Brand name glasses may be worn with small logo on frames or lenses. Logo must be same color as frames or lenses. Conservative wrap around sunglasses may be worn. Conservative, clear, slightly tinted or photosensitive lenses. Conservative lenses and frames (faddish styles and mirrored lenses prohibited). No sunglasses (to include darkened photosensitive lenses) in formation. Not worn around the neck or on top/back of head or exposed hanging on the uniform. Eyeglasses/sunglasses will be worn in the manner for which they were made.

Footwear, (Pg 89) Shined, in good repair. *EXCEPTION*: Boots that are designated as no-shine will be cleaned, polished, and in good repair.

Lanyard for access passes/badges/CAC, (Pg 91) Plain, dark blue or black lanyard, silver or plastic small conservative link chains, and clear plastic. Green may also be worn with the BDU. Must not present safety issue.

Necklaces, (Pg 90) Concealed under collar or undershirt; not visible.

Pager, cellular phone, and Personal Digital Assistant, (Pg 90) Must be solid or covered in black, silver, dark blue, or gray, and must be conservative. May be clipped to the left side of the waistband or purse or carried in left hand. Only one may be worn on the uniform belt. Members will not walk in uniform while using cell phones, radios, hands-free headsets unless required in the performance of official duties using a government issued device.

Pencils and pens, (Pg 90) Concealed. (***EXCEPTION:*** When carried in compartment of left BDU pocket not to exceed two.)

Religious Head Covering, (Pg 91) Indoors: Installation commander and chaplain may approve plain, dark blue or black religious head covering. Outdoors: Installation commander and chaplain may approve religious head covering which are concealed under headgear; requests for religious covering which are not concealed under headgear is processed according to Table 2.9.

Religious apparel and items, _(Other)_ (Pg 91) Concealed except when worn during religious services. Process requests according to Table 2.9. Do not wear approved items during parades, ceremonial details and functions or in official photos.

Rings, (Pg 89) A maximum of three rings on both hands combined. Wedding sets count as one ring. Will be worn only at the base of the finger. No thumb rings authorized.

Safety items, rain suits, snowmobile suits, (Pg 91) Worn while riding or operating two-wheeled vehicles. ***NOTE:*** Rollerblades, roller skates, skateboard, etc., are not authorized when in uniform.

Umbrella, (Pg 90) Plain black, carried in left hand.

Watch, _(1 only)_ (Pg 89) Conservative. Only one wristwatch is authorized for wear while in uniform.

Personal Grooming Standards (see notes) Table 1.5, (Pgs 12-15)

Beards, (M) (Pg 14) _Will not_ be worn except for health reasons when authorized by a commander on the advice of a medical official. If Commander authorizes, members will keep facial hair trimmed not to exceed 1/4 inch in length. Individuals granted a shaving waiver will not shave any facial hair. Commanders and supervisors will monitor progress in treatment to control these waivers. (See note 5).

Cosmetics, (W) (Pg 15) _Will be_ conservative and in good taste. _Will not be_ worn in field conditions.

Fingernails, (M & W) (Pg 15) _Will be_ clean and well-groomed. _Will not_ exceed 1/4 inch in length past tip of finger. Males are not authorized to wear nail polish. Interfere with duty performance or hinder proper fit of prescribed safety equipment or uniform items.

Hair, Overall Standard, (M & W) (Pg 12) _Will be_ clean, well-groomed and neat. _Will not_ contain excessive amount of grooming aids or touch eyebrows. Hair color/highlights/frosting must not be faddish. Examples of natural looking for human beings, Blonde/Brunette/ Red/Black/Grey) **_EXCEPTION:_** May be visible in front of women's flight cap.

Hairnets, (M & W) (Pg 14) _Will be_ worn as required for health and safety reasons. Made of cotton or a synthetic material; be of a conservative, solid color similar to the individual's hair color, be strong enough to support and control hair; and contain no metal fasteners. _Will not_ be worn when not performing related duties.

Hair Style, (M) (Pg 12) _Will be/have_ a tapered appearance on both sides and back, both with and without headgear. A tapered appearance is one that when viewed from any angle outlines the individual's hair so that it conforms to the shape of the head, curving inward to the natural termination point. Block cut permitted with tapered appearance. Cleanly shaven heads, military high-and-tight, or flat top haircuts are authorized. _Will not_ be worn in an extreme or fad style or in such a way that exceeds length or bulk standards or violates safety requirements. Protrude below the front band of properly worn headgear. Touch the ears and only closely cut or shaved hair on the back of the neck may touch the collar. Exceed 1 1/4 inches in bulk, regardless of length and exceed 1/4 inch at the natural termination point. Contain or have any visible foreign items attached to it.

Hair Style, (W) (Pg 13) _Will be/have_ styled to present a professional appearance. Allow the wear of conservative hairpins, combs, headbands, elastic bands, and barrettes. Hair pins and bands must match hair color. Long hair will be secured with no loose end. (see note 8.) Bangs, if worn, will not touch the eyebrows. Braids, micro-braids, and cornrows are authorized. However, must be solid color similar to the individual's hair color; conservative and not present a faddish appearance. Will not be worn in an extreme or fad style or violate safety requirements. Extend below any side of an invisible line drawn parallel to the ground at the bottom edge of the shirt collar regardless of length. Length will not be excessive. Include hair ornaments such as ribbons, beads, jeweled pins, or hair scrunchy. May not have shaved heads, military high-and-tight or flat-top haircuts. (Ban on faddish styles and cuts.) _Will not_ prevent proper wear of headgear, including helmet or chemical mask. Synthetic hair not authorized when not permitted by safety/mission requirements. Dreadlocks are not authorized. _**NOTE**_: Minimum length/bulk required is 1 inch not to exceed 3 inches in bulk and will not prevent proper wear of headgear, including helmet or chemical mask. (See notes 3 & 7).

Mustache, (M) (Pg 14) _Will be/have_ neatly trimmed. _Will not_ extend downward beyond the lip line of the upper lip or extend sideways beyond a vertical line drawn upward from both corners of the mouth. (See also "Sideburns" below).

Nail Polish /Lipstick, (W) (Pg 15) _Will be/have_ single color (compliment skin tone) and French manicure. (See note 6). _Will not_ no decorations; will not exceed 1/4 inch; _Will not_ wear shades of lipstick and nail polish that distinctly contrast with their complexion, that detract from the uniform, or that are extreme. Some examples of extreme colors include but are not limited to, purple, gold, blue, black, bright (fire-engine) red, and fluorescent colors.

Sideburns, (M) (Pg 14) _Will be/have_ neatly trimmed and tapered in the same manner as the haircut. Will be straight and of even width (not flared) and end in a clean-shaven horizontal line. _Will not_ extend below the lowest part of the exterior ear opening.

Wigs and Hairpieces, (M & W) (Pg 13) _Will be/have_ must meet AFI requirements (safe, functional, professional for all). In conformance with the same standards required for natural hair, be of good quality, and fit properly. _Will not_ exceed limits stated for natural hair. Worn by personnel engaged in aircraft flight line or in-flight operations. For medical justification related to baldness see note 5.

NOTES: (Pgs 15-16)
(All notes apply)
1. The items listed represent common appearance issues and are not all-inclusive.
2. Commanders do not have the authority to waive appearance and grooming standards except as identified.
3. Installation commanders will determine what is extreme or faddish. The Installation commander may delegate this authority to subordinate commanders to the squadron commander level.
4. During tours of less than 30 days, Reserve and Air National Guard (ANG) chaplains not on extended active duty may request a waiver for religious observance when consistent with their faith. For Air Force Reserve waiver-processing instructions see AFMAN 36-8001. For ANG waiver-processing instructions submit requests to NGB/HC, 1411 Jefferson Davis Hwy, Arlington, VA 22202-3231.
5. If due to a temporary medical condition i.e., radiation/chemotherapy and resulting in baldness, commanders will authorize the wear of the cancer approved American Society cap (black/tan).
6. Will not apply designs to nails or apply two-tone or multi-tone colors on duty excluding French manicure.
7. (Women) Medical waivers are required for situations that require baldness as a medical necessity while in uniform.
8. The intent of this item is that long hair should be styled in a manner that prevents loose ends from extending upward on the

head. (For example: when using the claw clip or hairpins, hair will not present the appearance of a "rooster tail"; when hair is in a bun, all loose ends must be tucked in and secured; when hair is in a pony tail, it must be pulled all the way through the elastic band and may hang naturally downward, not extending below the bottom of the collar). As with all hairstyles, a neat and professional image is essential

Men's and Women's Headgear, Figure 2.12, (Pg 32)

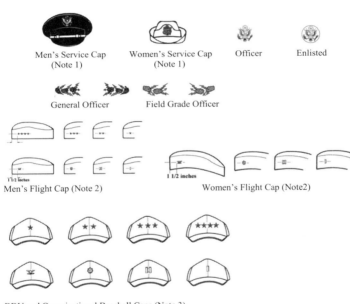

Men's Service Cap (Note 1)   Women's Service Cap (Note 1)   Officer   Enlisted

General Officer   Field Grade Officer

Men's Flight Cap (Note 2)   Women's Flight Cap (Note2)

BDU and Organizational Baseball Caps (Note 3)

NOTES: (Pgs 32-33)
1. Officers wear service cap insignia without circle with appropriate clouds and darts; enlisted wear service cap insignia with circle.

18

2. All Generals wear 1 inch stars on flight cap. 3/4 inch stars are optional if unable to wear the 1 inch stars. All other officers wear regular size (1 inch) metal grade insignia.

3. Officers wear the regular size cloth or subdued metal grade insignia on the BDU cap. Grade insignia will be centered vertically and horizontally. Colonel grade insignia is worn with the eagle's beak pointed towards the wearer's right shoulder (indicates the eagle is facing forward). MAJCOM commanders may authorize wear of the bright non-subdued grade insignia by officers on BDU caps while in garrison. *NOTE:* Chaplains may wear chaplains' insignia centered 1/2 inch above visor of BDU cap. General officers wear black stars.

4. Service caps - Mandatory for majors and above to maintain. Women are authorized to wear the men's service cap.

5. Flight cap - Women are authorized to wear the men's flight cap

When To Wear Headgear, Table 2.8, (Pg 92)

When to wear
- Outdoors.
- While operating two-wheeled vehicles. *EXCEPTION:* Not required when wearing safety headgear.

Do Not Wear
- When commanders specify for safety reasons.
- Indoors. (See notes 1 and 2.)

Optional Wear
- No-hat areas the installation commander designates in a supplement.

NOTES: (Pg 32)
1. *EXCEPTION:* Armed Security Forces personnel or others bearing arms while performing duties.
2. *EXCEPTION:* Public Health personnel wear headgear while performing facility inspections.

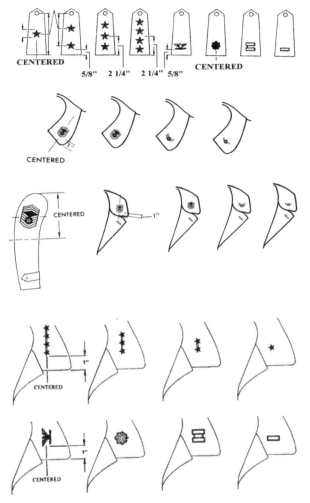

NOTE: Graphic above depicts placement on BDU/DCU shirt

NOTES: (Pg 35)

1. Full-Length Outergarments and Light Weight Blue Jacket. Officers center regular size (1 inch) metal rank insignia 5/8 inch from end of epaulet. All Generals wear 1 inch stars on all uniforms. 3/4 inch stars are optional if unable to wear the 1 inch stars. Enlisted personnel wear 3 1/2 or 4 inch (women) and 4 inch (men) sleeve chevron on sleeves or metal rank insignia on collar. Wear metal rank insignia centered 1 inch up from bottom collar, and parallel to outer edge.

2. Pullover and Cardigan Sweaters: Officers and Senior NCOs wear shoulder mark rank insignia. All other enlisted members wear metal rank insignia 5/8 inch from edge and centered. Center horizontally on the epaulet, with bottom of insignia 1 inch from shoulder seam.

3. BDU Field Jacket. Generals wear 1 inch black subdued cloth (point-to-point) or subdued metal pin-on grade insignia. 3/4 inch stars are optional if unable to wear the 1 inch black subdued cloth (point-to-point) or subdued metal pin-on grade insignia. All other officers center regular size subdued cloth or subdued metal pin-on grade insignia 5/8 inch from end of epaulet. Enlisted personnel wear 3 1/2, or 4 inch (women) or 4 inch (men) sleeve chevron halfway between shoulder seam and elbow when bent at 90-degree angle.

4. Gortex Jacket. Officers wear slide-on or pin-on subdued grade insignia. Enlisted wear slide-on subdued grade insignia. Rank insignia will appear on the front lapel of the gortex jacket.

Religious Apparel Waivers. Table 2.9 , (Pg 93)

Members: Submit request letter addressed to Installation Commander through Military Personnel Flight (MPF) Customer Service Element. Request letter includes a picture or description of the item, unit commander's endorsement, Installation Chaplain's endorsement.

Installation Chaplains: Ensure a base chaplain interviews member to assess whether the apparel is in keeping with doctrinal

21

or traditional observances of the member's faith. Endorse member's letter with findings.

Unit Commanders: Endorse request. Address affect on health or safety and impact on duties. Recommendations for disapproval should be unusual unless for safety or when precluded by military necessity. Requests should normally be approved unless approval would have an adverse impact on military readiness, unit cohesion, standards, or discipline. When requests are precluded by military necessity, commanders and supervisors should seek reasonable alternatives.

MPFs: Forward member's letter to installation commander and if appropriate, to member's MAJCOM/FOA, Director of Personnel/A-1 or J-1, as applicable. Notify member of final decision. File approval letter in the member's personnel folder.

Installation Commanders: May approve requests that are IAW Table 2.6, items 15 & 16. Recommend approval or disapproval when head covering cannot be concealed under headgear while outdoors or if they do not fall under the above item.

MAJCOM/FOA/DRU Director of Personnel: Recommend approval or disapproval. Forward to Air Force Uniform Division (AF/A1DO).

AF/A1DO: AF/A1DO recommends approval or disapproval to Air Force Deputy, Chief of Staff, Personnel (AF/A1). Returns AF/A1's decision through appropriate channels. Coordinates with AF/HC and AF/JA.

AF/A1: Approves or disapproves.

Wearing the Uniform (see notes), Table 1.3, (Pg 9)

Uniforms will be worn when: performing military duties (See notes 1 and 2)

Uniforms will not be worn when: **A.** uniform items do not meet Air Force specifications. **B.** participating in public speeches, interviews, picket lines, marches or rallies, or in any public demonstration when the Air Force sanction of the cause for which the activity is conducted may be implied. **C.** furthering political activities, private employment, or commercial interests. **D.** working in an off-duty civilian capacity. **E.** participating in civilian court proceedings when the conviction would bring discredit--at the discretion of installation commander. **F.** in civilian attire. For example: grade insignia, cap devices, badges and other U.S. or Air Force insignia, distinctive buttons, etc.

Uniform wear is optional when: **A.** departing from a military airfield on DoD aircraft or U.S. Government Commercial Contract Flights (service uniform combination) (See notes 3 and 4). **B.** departing from or arriving at commercial airports, or traveling on commercial contract flights (tie or tie tab optional) (See note 3 & 5). **C.** traveling in a foreign country. Consult the DoD Foreign Clearance Guide. **D.** attending off-duty education conducted off a military installation.

NOTES: **(Pgs 9-10)**
1. On other Services' installations, comply with order of dress for that Service, within Air Force standards.
2. TDY personnel will comply with local policies established at each TDY location, within Air Force standards.
3. Those choosing to wear civilian clothing will ensure it is neat, clean, and warm enough for in-flight operations and appropriate for the mode of travel and destination. Examples of inappropriate clothing include: ripped, torn, frayed, or patched clothing; tank tops, shorts, short skirts, undergarments worn as outergarment, bathing suits, sandals, and any garments which are revealing or contain obscene, profane, or lewd words or drawings.
4. The Battle Dress Uniform is an acceptable uniform when traveling between military installations.

23

5. Air Force personnel may not wear their military uniforms when using frequent flyer miles to upgrade to business or first class. Thus, even when an upgrade to business or first class accommodations is legitimate, military personnel should avoid wearing the uniform to avoid the public perception of the misuse of government travel resources, which generates unnecessary complaints.

6. Officers and Enlisted: Do not wear or mix unique uniform items with civilian clothes. These items are those unique to the uniform. They include grade insignia, cap devices, badges and other U. S. or Air Force insignia, such as items with the "wing and star" design, and so forth. *Exception:* Tie tacks and lapel pins when wearing business attire authorized.

7. General Officers are encouraged to wear a combination of blue uniform when traveling on commercial aircraft.

8. Air Force personnel may wear civilian attire on commercial aircraft or a combination of blue uniform if they prefer.

9. Utility uniforms (BDU and flight suits) are not authorized for travel on commercial aircraft.

10. Uniform of the Day (BDU and flight suits) is authorized for traveling MILAIR.

Wear of Desert Camouflage Uniform (DCU) (see notes), Table 1.4, (Pg 11)

Wear DCU when

- CSAS-approved uniform for wear while traveling to and from CENTCOM AOR
- Personnel deploying or PCSing to the AOR are allowed to wear conservative civilian attire, DCU to/from the AOR (See note 1)
- May also be worn on U.S. FLAG commercial flights in CONUS while traveling between the aerial port and the airman's authorized rest and recuperation leave location
- Traveling enroute between CONUS locations on a commercial aircraft, and/or
- On military aircraft or government chartered aircraft enroute (CONUS or overseas)

- DCUs may also be worn on the commercial flights in CONUS while traveling between the aerial port and the airman's authorized rest and recuperation leave location
- No other travel in DCUs on any commercial carrier is authorized (ordinary leave, TDY outside AOR, etc)
- Uniform for contingency situations (See note 2)

NOTES: (Pg 11)

1. Provided they are traveling enroute between CONUS locations on a U.S. Flag commercial aircraft, bus, or train and/or on military aircraft or government chartered aircraft, bus, or train enroute (CONUS or Overseas)

2. One set of conservative civilian attire is to be packed in carry-on luggage in order to accommodate for contingency situations. Airmen will maintain proper uniform, personal appearance, and hygiene standards during travel at all times.

3. No DCUs wear. The only exception per the CSAF is BC3 enroute personnel training.

Men's Service Dress, Figure 2.1, (Pg 17)

NOTES: **(Pg 18)**

1. Center metallic nametag on right side between the sleeve seam and the lapel. Bottom of nametag will be parallel with bottom of ribbons. Became mandatory 1 January 2004.

2. Place U.S. insignia halfway up the seam, resting on but not over it. Bottom of insignia is horizontal with the ground. Circles will be worn around the U. S. Insignias. Implementation date 1 January 2007.

3. Center ribbons resting on (but not over) edge of pocket. Wear all ribbons and devices. See Figure 4.3 for arrangement of ribbons.

4. Air Force members are highly encouraged to wear their current occupational badge. Aeronautical and chaplain badges are mandatory, others are optional. Wear only mid-size or regular badges, do not mix sizes. Center aeronautical, occupational, or miscellaneous badge 1/2 inch above the top row of ribbons. Center

26

additional badge 1/2 inch above first one. Center duty or miscellaneous badge 1 1/2 inches below top of welt pocket and centered, and/or on right side centered 1 1/2 inch below the nametag. Center a third badge 1/2 inch above the nametag. No more than 4 badges will be worn at one time. This includes Command Insignia. ***EXCEPTIONS:*** Missile badge is only worn 1/2 inch below top of welt pocket and centered. Excellence-In-Competition badge is worn centered on the welt pocket.

5. Air Force Command Insignia: Current commander center 1/2 inch above nametag; graduated commander center 1/2 inch below nametag. If duty badges are worn with the command insignia (graduated commander), center the duty badge 1/2 inch below command insignia. AF Command **insignia is mandatory.**

6. Officers: Center regular size grade insignia 5/8 inch from end of epaulet. Generals wear 1 inch stars on all uniforms. 3/4 inch stars are optional if unable to wear the 1 inch stars. Enlisted: Center 4 inch sleeve chevron halfway between shoulder seam and elbow bent at 90-degree angle.

7. Necktie is mandatory. Center optional tie tack or tie clasp (Air Force symbol, grade insignia, or "wing and star") between bottom edge of knot and bottom tip of tie.

8. Individuals, at their discretion, may sew down pockets but no local policy will be established to make it mandatory.

Men's Short-Sleeved Shirt, Figure 2.4, (Pg 21)

NOTES: **(Pgs 21-22)**

1. Center nametag on (but not over) edge of right pocket.

2. Center ribbons resting on (but not over) edge of pocket between the left and right edges. Ribbons are optional. If worn, all ribbons and devices will be worn. See Figure 4.3 for arrangement of ribbons.

3. Air Force members are highly encouraged to wear their current occupational badge. Aeronautical and chaplain badges are mandatory, others are optional. Wear only mid-size or regular badges, do not mix sizes. Center aeronautical, occupational, or miscellaneous badge 1/2 inch above ribbons or pocket if not wearing ribbons. Center additional badge 1/2 inch above the first one. Center duty or miscellaneous badge on lower portion of left pocket between left and right edges and bottom of flap and pocket, and/or on right pocket between left and right edges and bottom of flap and pocket. ***EXCEPTIONS:*** Missile badge is only worn centered on left pocket. Excellence-In-Competition badge is worn centered on top edge of left pocket flap.

28

4. Air Force Command Insignia: Current commanders wear the insignia centered 1/2 inch above the nametag. Graduated commanders, when worn, wear the insignia centered below the nametag between the nametag and the button of the right pocket flap. AF Command Insignia is mandatory.

5. Officers place shoulder mark insignia as close as possible to shoulder seam. Enlisted personnel center 3 1/2 inch sleeve chevrons halfway between shoulder seam and bottom edge of sleeve. Senior noncommissioned officers may wear shoulder mark insignia (as close to as possible shoulder seam) or chevrons.

6. Necktie is optional. Center optional tie tack or tie clasp (Air Force symbol, grade insignia, or "wing and star") between bottom edge of knot and bottom tip of tie. Tip of tie must cover a portion of the belt buckle but cannot extend below the bottom of belt buckle.

7. Individuals, at their discretion, may sew down pockets but no local policy will be established to make it mandatory.

NOTES: (Pgs 22-23)

1. Center nametag on (but not over) edge of right pocket.

2. Center ribbons resting on (but not over) edge of pocket between the left and right edges. Ribbons are optional. If worn, all ribbons and devices must be worn. See Figure 4.3 for arrangement of ribbons.

3. Air Force members are highly encouraged to wear their current occupational badge. Aeronautical and chaplain badges are mandatory, others are optional. Wear only mid-size or regular badges, do not mix sizes. Center aeronautical, occupational, or miscellaneous badge 1/2 inch above ribbons or pocket if not wearing ribbons. Center additional badge 1/2 inch above the first one. Center duty or miscellaneous badge on lower portion of left pocket between left and right edges and bottom of flap and pocket, and/or on right pocket between left and right edges and bottom of flap and pocket. **EXCEPTIONS:** Missile badge is only worn centered on left pocket. Excellence-In-Competition badge is worn centered on top edge of left pocket flap.

4. Air Force Command Insignia: Current commanders wear the insignia centered 1/2 inch above the nametag. Graduated commanders, when worn, wear the insignia centered below the nametag between the nametag and the button of the right pocket flap. AF Command Insignia is mandatory.

5. Officers place shoulder mark insignia as close as possible to shoulder seam. Enlisted personnel center 3 1/2 inch sleeve chevrons halfway between shoulder seam and elbow bent at 90-degree angle. Senior noncommissioned officers may wear shoulder mark insignia (as close as possible to shoulder seam) or chevrons.

6. Necktie is mandatory. Center optional tie tack or tie clasp (Air Force symbol, grade insignia, or "wing and star") between bottom edge of knot and bottom tip of tie. Tip of tie must cover a portion of the belt buckle but cannot extend below the bottom of belt buckle.

7. Individuals, at their discretion, may sew down pockets but no local policy will be established to make it mandatory.

Men's Mess Dress Uniform, (Pg 19)

NOTES: **(Pg 19)**

1. Nametag and headgear is not worn. Saluting is not required when outdoors.

2. Air Force members are highly encouraged to wear their current occupational badge. Aeronautical and chaplain badges are mandatory, others are optional. Wear only mid-size or regular badges, do not mix sizes. Center aeronautical, occupational, or miscellaneous badge 1/2 inch above top row of medals or when not authorized medals, midway between shoulder and top button. Wear second badge 1/2 inch above first badge when authorized. Center duty or miscellaneous badge 1/2 inch below bottom row of medals or comparable position when no medals are authorized. Center a second badge on the right side in same relative position as those badges worn on left, this includes Missile and Excellence-In-Competition badges. Miniature duty badges will be worn (***EXAMPLES***: Presidential, OSD, Joint Staff, HAF).

3. Center all miniature medals between lapel and arm seam and midway between top shoulder seam and top button of jacket. See Table 4.1 for arrangement of medals.

4. Air Force Command Insignia: Worn on the right side of the uniform. Current commander center insignia adjacent to top of miniature medals; graduated commanders lower insignia adjacent to bottom row of miniature medals. AF Command Insignia is mandatory.

5. Wear white formal long shirt.

6. Blue satin bow tie is mandatory.

7. Wear cummerbund with pleats up around waist, half-way between pants and shirt.

8. Wear matching cufflinks and studs as a set. Wear "wing and star" design, satin finish with AF symbol or plain silver highly polished cufflinks.

9. Officers place shoulder board insignia as close as possible to shoulder seam. Enlisted personnel center 4 inch sleeve chevron halfway between shoulder seam and elbow bent at 90-degree angle.

NOTES: (Pg 20)

1. Nametag and headgear is not worn. Saluting when outdoors is not required.

2. Center ribbons resting on (but not over) edge of welt pocket and between left and right edges. Wear all ribbons and devices. See Figure 4.3 for arrangement of ribbons.

3. Place U.S. insignia halfway up the lapel seam, resting on but not over it. Bottom of insignia is horizontal with the ground. Circles will be worn around the U. S. Insignias. Implementation date 1 January 2007.

4. Air Force members are highly encouraged to wear their current occupational badge. Aeronautical and chaplain badges are mandatory, others are optional. Wear only mid-size or regular badges, do not mix sizes. Center aeronautical, occupational, or miscellaneous badge 1/2 inch above the top row of ribbons. Center additional badge 1/2 inch above first one. Center duty or miscellaneous badge 1 1/2 inches below top of welt pocket and centered, and/or on right side centered between arm seam and lapel, with bottom edge of badge parallel to top of welt pocket.

EXCEPTIONS: Missile badge is only worn 1 1/2 inches below top of welt pocket and centered. Excellence-In-Competition badge is worn centered on the welt pocket.

5. Center 4 inch sleeve chevron halfway between shoulder seam and elbow bent at 90-degree angle.

6. Herringbone tie is mandatory. Center optional tie tack or tie clasp (Air Force symbol, grade insignia, or "wing and star") between bottom edge of knot and bottom tip of tie.

7. Wear with white long or short-sleeved shirt as described in Table 2.1.

8. Individuals, at their discretion, may sew down pockets but no local policy will be established to make it mandatory.

Items for Men's Service and Dress Uniforms (see note), Table 2.1, (Pgs 48-55)

THIS INCLUDES SERVICE DRESS, MESS DRESS, FORMAL DRESS AND SEMI-FORMAL DRESS

Accouterments (Service Dress, Long-Sleeved Shirt, Short-Sleeved Shirt, Mess Dress, Formal Dress, Semi-Formal), (Pg 55): Figure of each uniform shows proper placement of accouterments and gives a description of each. The finish of all accouterments must match.

Belt and Buckle, (Service Dress, Long-Sleeved Shirt, Short-Sleeved Shirt, Semi-Formal), (Pg 51): Silver-tip end of the belt extends beyond the buckle facing the wearer's left; no blue fabric shows. Woven cotton web or elastic, solid or woven, belt with matching silver-color metal tip and buckle chrome-like finish. *General officers* may wear the "wing and star" design, shiny finish emblem and belt buckle.

Cufflinks, (Service Dress, Long-Sleeved Shirt, Mess Dress, Semi-Formal), (Pg 55): "wing and star" design, satin finish with AF symbol or plain silver highly polished cufflinks (mandatory with mess dress; optional with long-sleeved shirts).

Cummerbund (Mess Dress), (Pg 55): Blue satin, worn with open edge of pleats facing upward. Pleated without design.

34

Earmuffs, (Black), (Service Dress, Mess Dress, Formal Dress, Semi-Formal), (Pg 54): (commercial design of any material). Wear only with authorized outergarments and service dress uniform.

Footwear

Combat Boots (Black/Jungle Boot), (Service Dress, Long-Sleeved Shirt, Short-Sleeved Shirt), (Pg 51): With or without safety toe; must have a plain rounded toe or rounded capped toe with or without perforated seam; zipper or elastic inserts are optional; no designs. High-gloss or patent finish optional.

Dress Boots (Black), (Service Dress, Long-Sleeved Shirt, Short-Sleeved Shirt), (Pg 51): With rounded plain or rounded capped toe; zipper or elastic inserts optional; no design; sole will not exceed 1/2 inch in thickness and shoe heels will not exceed 1 inch in height (measured from the inside front of the heel). High-gloss or patent finish optional.

Low Quarters (Black), (Service Dress, Long-Sleeved Shirt, Short-Sleeved Shirt, Mess Dress, Formal Dress, Semi-Formal),
(Pg 51): Oxford; lace-up style with a plain rounded toe or a plain rounded capped toe; with or without seam and; without perforation or design; sole will not exceed 1/2 inch in thickness and the heel will not exceed 1 inch in height (measured from the inside front of the heel); may have low wedge heel; smooth or scotch-grained leather or man-made material; high-gloss or patent finish optional.

Socks (Black), (Service Dress, Long-Sleeved Shirt, Short-Sleeved Shirt, Mess Dress, Formal Dress, Semi-Formal), (Pg 52): Plain without design. Plain white socks may be worn with combat boots or dress boots. Wear black socks over the white socks to preclude white socks from showing.

Headgear

Blue Winter Cap, (Service Dress, Mess Dress, Formal Dress, Semi-Formal), (Pg 54): Only with full-length outergarments (ie; rain jacket, not worn with lightweight blue jacket or cardigan/pullover sweater). Commercial design with ear and neck flaps, ribbon tie or strap with covered metal snap fastener; grade insignia is not worn; wool and polyester serge mouton, snap fastener cover.

Flight Cap (Men's), (Service Dress, Long-Sleeved Shirt, Short-Sleeved Shirt), (Pg 54): Slightly to the wearer's right with vertical crease of the cap in line with the center of the forehead, in a straight line with the nose; the cap extends approximately 1 inch from the eyebrows in the front, opening of cap is to the rear; if not worn, tuck under the belt on wearer's left side, between first and second belt loops; cap will not fold over belt. Cap has dark blue colored edge braid for enlisted personnel, silver-colored edge braid for general officers, and silver and blue in a diamond pattern edge braid for all other officers; all shades and material of hat are authorized with any uniform combination. Mandatory for all male personnel. Cap will not be tucked under epaulets

Men's Service Cap, (Service Dress, Long-Sleeved Shirt, Short-Sleeved Shirt), (Pg 54): Squarely on the head with no hair protruding in front of the cap; large size hat insignia, officer or enlisted as appropriate is centered on the front of the cap. Visor-type service cap is banded with dark blue 1 3/4 inch braid; has front black chin strap; an optional version with braid of an open mesh construction, and an optional black leather back strap. *Service cap mandatory*

Watch Cap (Knit, Black or Navy Blue), (Service Dress), (Pg 54): Commercial design. Wear when approved by installation commanders and only with authorized outergarments and service dress uniform. Grade insignia is not worn.

Outergarments
General (Pg 52): Worn outdoors only, removed in an office environment, except as noted below. Use good judgment in choosing appropriate garments for wear based on weather conditions and duties. May wear with civilian clothes if grade insignia is removed. See Figure 2.9 for grade insignia placement.

Coats

All-Weather Coat-Blue, (Service Dress, Long-Sleeved Shirt, Short-Sleeved Shirt, Mess Dress, Formal Dress, Semi-Formal), (Pg 53): Loose enough to fit over service coats; shoulders fit loose enough to accommodate shoulders of service coat without binding at armholes when moving arms. Sleeves will extend 1/2 inch beyond the sleeve of the service coat; length of coat not shorter than 1/2 inch below the bottom of the knee nor longer than 6 inches below the back crease of the knee; neck button may be left unbuttoned. Water resistant double-breasted with belt and buckle, button throat closure, shoulder straps, sleeve straps, center back vent, facing tabs, and zip-out liner. May wear over pullover and cardigan sweaters.

(Enlisted)

(Service Dress), (Pg 48): Polyester and wool blend, serge weave; semi-drape, single-breasted with three buttons, no epaulets, one welt pocket on upper left side, and two lower pocket flaps. With arms hanging naturally, sleeves will end approximately 1/4 inch from the heel of the thumb. Ensure the bottom edge of coat extends 3 to 3 1/2 inches below the top of the thigh; sleeves and lapel will be roll-pressed. Wear 4-inch chevron. Coat and trouser must match in shade and material.

(Semi-Formal), (Pg 48): White shirt is worn without nametag and hat.

Mess Dress Jacket, (Mess Dress), (Pg 49): Mandatory for officers and optional for enlisted. Worn for social functions of general or official nature (black tie affairs), tuxedo is civilian equivalent. Semi-fitted; sleeves will end approximately 1/4 inch from heel of thumb; single-breasted, straight back with three "wing and star" buttons diagonally on both sides and a front link chain closure with button on each end; satin shawl collar and lapels; center back length will be 3 1/2 inches to 4 inches below natural waistline; *General Officers* wear 3/4 inch wide silver sleeve braid 3 inches from end of sleeve; all other *officers* wear 1/2 inch wide silver sleeve braid 3 inches from end of sleeve; Enlisted personnel women wear 3 1/2 or 4 inch chevron and men wear 4 inch chevron. Jacket and trousers must match in shade and material.

(Officer), (Service Dress), (Pg 48): Polyester and wool blend, serge weave; semi-drape, single-breasted with three buttons, one welt pocket on upper left side, and two lower pocket flaps. With arms hanging naturally, sleeves will end approximately 1/4 inch from the heel of the thumb. Ensure the bottom edge of coat extends 3 to 3 1/2 inches below the top of the thigh; sleeves and lapel will be roll-pressed. Colonels and below wear regular size metal grade insignia on epaulets and 1/2 inch blue sleeve braid 3 inches from end of sleeve. *General Officers:* Wear 1 inch stars on all uniforms. 3/4 inch stars are optional if unable to wear the 1 inch stars. Wear 1 1/2 inch blue sleeve braid 3 inches from end of sleeve. Coat and trouser will match in shade and material.

Top Coat (Blue, Double-Breasted), (Service Dress, Long-Sleeved Shirt, Short-Sleeved Shirt, Mess Dress, Formal Dress, Semi-Formal), (Pg 53): Stand-up collar, six-button front, shoulder epaulets with buttons, sleeve straps with buckles. Water resistant, double-breasted with belt and buckle, button throat closure, shoulder straps, sleeve straps, center back vent, facing tabs, and zip-out liner. Coat will fit loosely enough to accommodate shoulders of a uniform without binding at armholes when arms are moved; sleeves will extend 1/2 inch beyond service coat sleeves; loose fitting with bottom of coat extending to between bottom of knee cap and mid-calf; may wear over pullover and cardigan sweaters.

Blue Cardigan, (Long-Sleeved Shirt, Short-Sleeved Shirt), (Pg 52): Acrylic wool blend with long, cuffed sleeves; indoor or outdoor garment; buttoned or unbuttoned indoors; must be buttoned outdoors; when buttoned, must be completely buttoned; tie is optional; wear collar of shirt inside or outside sweater; not exposed when wearing another outergarment.

Lightweight Blue Jacket, (Long-Sleeved Shirt, Short-Sleeved Shirt), (Pg 52): Indoor or outdoor garment; Zip up at least halfway; not authorized for wear when service dress uniform is designated or more appropriate. May wear over pullover and cardigan sweaters. Partially lined, water repellent, waist length, zipper front, with two slant pockets and knitted cuffs and waistband; worn with or without insulated liner. The AF Symbol may be embroidered on the jacket at member's expense. May not be worn with civilian clothes if the AF symbol is embroidered on the jacket.

Pullover Sweater, (Long-Sleeved Shirt, Short-Sleeved Shirt), (Pg 52): All wool or wool/acrylic blend, V-neck, long-sleeved, with cuffed sleeves. Indoor or outdoor garment; tie is optional; wear collar of shirt inside or outside sweater; not exposed when wearing another outergarment. Place metallic nametag on wearer's right side with the bottom of the nametag level centered between the middle of the sleeve seam and the seam of the neckline; position at an appropriate level down from shoulder seam. *NOTE:* Installation commanders retain the option to require the wear of a tie with all uniform combinations based on specific circumstances.

Gloves or Mittens (Black), (Service Dress, Mess Dress, Formal Dress, Semi-Formal), (Pg 53): Leather, knitted, tricot or suede, or a combination of leather, knitted, tricot, and suede.

Scarf (Black), (Service Dress, Mess Dress, Formal Dress, Semi-Formal), (Pg 53): Tucked in with authorized outergarments. Not authorized with pullover and blue cardigan sweaters when worn as outgarments. Will not exceed 10 inches in width; all wool or cotton simplex, with or without napped surface.

Shirts
Blue Long-Sleeved, (Service Dress, Long-Sleeved Shirt), (Pg 50): Necktie is mandatory unless worn just with a sweater. Collar of shirt shows 1/4 or 1/2 inch above coat collar; with arms hanging naturally, sleeves extend to heel of thumb. It

has two pleated pockets and convertible cuffs; tapered fit is optional; military creases are prohibited. Blue polyester herringbone twill tie is mandatory if wearing service dress coat.

White Long-Sleeved:
(Mess Dress), (Pg 50): Conventional dress type with turndown collar and French cuffs with pleats. Blue satin bow tie mandatory. Military creases prohibited.

(Formal Dress), (Pg 50): White. Commercial design full dress with wing collar; military creases prohibited. White bow tie mandatory.

(Semi-Formal), (Pg 50): Enlisted only; Plain knitted or woven, commercial type with short or medium point collar, without design with button or French cuff; military creases are prohibited. Blue polyester herringbone twill tie is mandatory.

Blue Short-Sleeved: (Service Dress, Short-Sleeved Shirt, Semi-Formal), (Pg 50): Tie is optional unless worn with service dress uniform (blue shirt) or semi-formal (white shirt). Collar of shirt shows 1/4 or 1/2 inch above coat collar; with arms bent at a 90-degree angle, sleeve should barely touch or come within 1 inch of the forearm; tapered fit. It has two pleated pockets; military creases are prohibited. White shirt is worn with semi-formal uniform only.

Studs, (Mess Dress), (Pg 55): Plain silver highly polished or satin finished.

Suspenders, (Mess Dress), (Pg 55): Solid white, blue, or black; will not be visible.

Tie
(Service Dress, Long-Sleeved Shirt, Short-Sleeved Shirt, Semi-Formal), (Pg 51): Blue polyester herringbone twill. Wear with service dress coat.

(Long-Sleeved Shirt, Short-Sleeved Shirt), (Pg 51):
Blue. Without design or sheen, 2 to 3 inches wide; may be tapered at the center with a pointed end or untapered with a square end. Polyester or wool, synthetic, or blends; woven and pre-tied ties are optional.

Bow Tie

(Formal Dress), (Pg 51): White, with square ends.

(Mess Dress), (Pg 51): Blue satin, 5 to 5 1/2 inches long and 2 1/2 inches wide, with square ends without design.

Trousers

(Service Dress, Long-Sleeved Shirt, Short-Sleeved Shirt, Semi-Formal), (Pg 50): Trim-fitted with no bunching at waist or bagging at seat; knee and bottom leg widths not altered beyond current specifications for the waist size; front of trouser legs rests on the front of shoe or boot with a slight break in the crease; back of trouser legs will be approximately 7/8 inch longer than the front. Full cut, straight hanging and without cuffs; available in 100% polyester, polyester wool tropical, and polyester or wool blend, serge weave.

(Mess Dress, Formal Dress), (Pg 50): Without cuffs, high-rise with side pockets, 7/8-inch blue striping, no pleats.

Undergarments – Mandatory (Service Dress, Long-Sleeved Shirt, Short-Sleeved Shirt, Mess Dress, Formal Dress, Semi-Formal), (Pg 55): Wear undershorts and white undershirt (V-neck or athletic style) with all service and dress uniforms; the white crew-neck style undershirt is authorized only when wearing closed collar service and dress uniforms. Undershirt will be tucked into trousers.

Vest, (Formal Dress), (Pg 55): White, single-breasted, low-cut, rolled collar vest with pointed collar. Wear instead of a cummerbund.

NOTES: **(Pg 55)**
1. The mess dress is optional for enlisted personnel and mandatory for officers. Only officers wear the formal dress. Only enlisted personnel wear the semi-formal dress.

Women's Service Dress Uniform, (Pg 36)

NOTES: **(Pg 36)**
1. Center metallic nametag on right side between the sleeve seam and the lapel. Bottom of nametag will be parallel with bottom of ribbons. Mandatory as of 1 January 2004.
2. Place U.S. insignia halfway up the seam, resting on but not over it. Bottom of insignia is horizontal with the ground. Circles will be worn around the U. S. Insignias. Implementation date 1 January 2007.
3. Center ribbons resting on (but not over) edge of welt pocket. Wear all ribbons and devices. See Figure 4.3 for arrangement of ribbons.
4. Air Force members are highly encouraged to wear their current occupational badge. Aeronautical and chaplain badges are mandatory, others are optional. Wear only mid-size or regular badges, do not mix sizes. Center aeronautical, occupational, or miscellaneous badge 1/2 inch above the top row of ribbons. Center additional badge 1/2 inch above first one. If placing duty or identification badges above the nametag, center badges 1/2 inch above nametag and centered 1/2 inch apart. Large badges are authorized. (*EXAMPLES*: Presidential, OSD, Joint Staff, HAF). Center two identification badges 1/2 inch above nametag and centered 1/2 inch apart. *EXCEPTIONS:* The Missile and Excellence-in-Competition badge is worn 1 1/2 inches below top of welt pocket and centered or on the right side 1/2 inch above nametag.
5. Air Force Command Insignia: Current commander center 1/2 inch above nametag; graduated commander center 1/2 inch below

nametag. If duty badges are worn they will be worn 1/2 inch above command insignia (current commander). AF Command insignia is mandatory.

6. Officers: Center regular size grade insignia 5/8 inch from end of epaulet. Generals wear 1 inch stars on all uniforms. 3/4 inch stars are optional if unable to wear the 1 inch stars. Enlisted: Center 3 1/2 or 4 inch sleeve chevron halfway between shoulder seam and elbow bent at 90-degree angle.

7. Tie tab is mandatory.

Women's Short-Sleeved Blouse, (Pg 39)

NOTES: (Pg 39)

1. Center nametag on right side, even to within 1 1/2 inches higher or lower than the first exposed button.

2. Center ribbons on left side parallel with ground. Align bottom of the ribbons with the bottom of the nametag. Ribbons are optional. If worn, all ribbons and devices will be worn. See Figure 4.3 for arrangement of ribbons.

3. Air Force members are highly encouraged to wear their current occupational badge. Aeronautical and chaplain badges are mandatory, others are optional. Center aeronautical, occupational, or miscellaneous badge 1/2 inch above the ribbons. When not wearing ribbons, center badge parallel to the nametag. Center additional badge 1/2 inch above first one. If placing duty or miscellaneous badges above the nametag, center an additional badge 1/2 inch above the first one. The Missile Badge and Excellence-In-Competition badge is worn 1 1/2 inches below bottom of ribbons and centered or on the right side 1/2 inch above nametag.

4. Center duty or miscellaneous badge 1/2 inch above nametag.

5. Air Force Command Insignia: Current commander center 1/2 inch above nametag; graduated commander center 1/2 inch below nametag. If duty badges are worn they will be worn 1/2 inch above command insignia (current commander). AF Command insignia is mandatory.

6. Officers place shoulder mark insignia as close as possible to shoulder seam. Generals wear 1 inch stars on all uniforms. 3/4 inch stars are optional if unable to wear the 1 inch stars. Enlisted personnel center 3 1/2 inch sleeve chevron halfway between shoulder seam and bottom edge of sleeve. Senior NCOs wear shoulder mark insignia or chevrons.

7. Tie tab is optional.

Women's Long-Sleeved Blouse, Figure 2.18, (Pg 40)

***NOTES:* (Pgs 40-41)**
1. Center nametag on right side, even to within 1 1/2 inches higher or lower than the first exposed button.
2. Center ribbons on left side parallel with ground. Align bottom of the ribbons with the bottom of the nametag. Ribbons are optional. If worn, all ribbons and devices will be worn. See Figure 4.3 for arrangement of ribbons.
3. Air Force members are highly encouraged to wear their current occupational badge. Aeronautical and chaplain badges are mandatory, others are optional. Center aeronautical, occupational, or miscellaneous badge 1/2 inch above the ribbons. When not wearing ribbons, center badge parallel to the nametag. Center additional badge 1/2 inch above first one. Center duty or miscellaneous badge on the right side centered 1/2 inch above the nametag. If placing duty or miscellaneous badges above the nametag, center an additional badge 1/2 inch above the first one.

44

The Missile Badge and Excellence-In-Competition badge is worn 1 1/2 inches below bottom of ribbons and centered or on the right side 1/2 inch above nametag.

4. Center duty or miscellaneous badge 1/2 inch above nametag

5. Air Force Command Insignia: Current commander center 1/2 inch above nametag; graduated commander center 1/2 inch below nametag. If duty badges are worn they will be worn 1/2 inch above command insignia (current commander). AF Command insignia is mandatory.

6. Officers place shoulder mark insignia as close as possible to shoulder seam. Generals wear 1 inch stars on all uniforms. 3/4 inch stars are optional if unable to wear the 1 inch stars. Enlisted personnel center 3 1/2 inch sleeve chevron halfway between shoulder seam and elbow when bent at 90-degree angle. Senior NCOs wear shoulder mark insignia or chevrons.

7. Tie tab is mandatory.

Women's Mess Dress Uniform, (Pg 37)

NOTES: **(Pg 37)**

1. Nametag and headgear is not worn. Saluting is not required when outdoors.

2. Center all miniature medals between lapel and arm seam and midway between top of shoulder seam horizontal with the ground. See Table 4.1 for arrangement of medals.

3. Air Force members are highly encouraged to wear their current occupational badge. Aeronautical and chaplain badges are mandatory, others are optional. Wear only mid-size or regular badges, do not mix sizes. Center aeronautical, occupational, or miscellaneous badge 1/2 inch above top row of medals or when not authorized medals, midway between shoulder and top button. Wear second badge 1/2 inch above first badge when authorized. When wearing one identification badge, center the badge on the right side with the top of the badge parallel to the top row of medals. (***EXAMPLES***: Presidential, OSD, Joint Staff, HAF). Center two identification badges on the right side adjacent to the miniature medals on left side and centered 1/2 inch apart. **EXCEPTIONS:**

The Missile and Excellence-in-Competition badge is worn 1 1/2 inches below top of welt pocket and centered.

4. Air Force Command Insignia: Worn on the right side of the uniform. Current commander center insignia 1/2 above the identification badge on the right side adjacent to the aeronautical, occupational, or miscellaneous badge; graduated commanders center insignia 1/2 inch below identification badge on the right side. AF Command Insignia is mandatory.

5. Cufflinks are optional. When wearing matching cufflinks and studs as a set, wear "wing and star" design, satin finish with AF symbol or plain silver highly polished cufflinks. (Black studs are not authorized)

6. Officers place shoulder board insignia as close as possible to shoulder seam (buttons on the shoulder boards do not have to match the buttons on the jacket). Enlisted personnel center 3 1/2 or 4 inch sleeve chevron halfway between shoulder seam and elbow bent at 90-degree angle.

7. Tie tab is mandatory. Wear blue satin invert V-tie tab.

8. Wear white formal long-sleeved blouse.

9. Wear cummerbund with pleats up around waist, half-way between skirt and blouse.

Women's Semi-Formal Dress Uniform (Enlisted only), (Pg 38)

NOTES: **(Pg 38)**

1. Nametag and headgear is not worn. Saluting is not required when outdoors.

2. Center ribbons resting on (but not over) edge of welt pocket and between left and right edges. Wear all ribbons and devices. See Figure 4.3 for arrangement of ribbons.

3. Place U.S. insignia halfway up the seam, resting on but not over it. Bottom of insignia is horizontal with the ground. Circles will be worn around the U. S. Insignias. Implementation date was 1 January 2007.

4. Air Force members are highly encouraged to wear their current occupational badge. Aeronautical and chaplain badges are mandatory, others are optional. Wear only mid-size or regular badges, do not mix sizes. Center aeronautical, occupational, or miscellaneous badge 1/2 inch above top row of ribbons. Center additional badge 1/2 inch above first one. Center duty or miscellaneous badge 1 1/2 inches below top of welt pocket and/or on right side centered between arm seam and lapel, with bottom edge of badge parallel with top of welt pocket. If placing duty or miscellaneous badges on the right side, center additional duty badge 1/2 inch above the first. **EXCEPTIONS:** The Missile and Excellence-in-Competition badge is worn 1 1/2 inches below top of welt pocket and centered or on the right side.

5. Center 3 1/2 or 4 inch sleeve chevron halfway between shoulder seam and elbow bent at 90-degree angle.

6. Tie tab is mandatory.

7. Worn with white long or short-sleeved blouse only. Polyester or cotton, princess line, button-front, with small pointed collar; wear with blue satin inverted V-tie tab with or without self-fastening tails, as described in Table 2.3.

8. Slacks are not authorized.

Maternity Dress Section
Maternity Blouse
Maternity Long-Sleeved Blouse, Figure 2.23, (Pg 46)

(Long-Sleeved Maternity Blouse, Short-Sleeved Maternity Blouse), (Pg 65): Blue long or short-sleeved, pointed collar with blue inverted V-tie tab with or without self-fastening tails. Tie tab mandatory with long-sleeves, optional with short-sleeves. Unseamed with fuller body to accommodate pregnancy. Button epaulets over jumper only when wearing shoulder mark insignia. Military creases are prohibited.

(Maternity Service Dress, Maternity Jumper, Long-Sleeved Maternity Blouse), (Pg 66): Blue long-sleeved with pointed collar with blue inverted V-tie tab with or without self-fastening tails. Enlisted personnel wear sleeve chevrons only; officers wear shoulder mark insignia. Button epaulets over jumper only when wearing shoulder mark insignia. Military creases are prohibited.

(Maternity Jumper, Long-Sleeved Maternity Blouse, Mess Dress, Semi-Formal), (Pg 66): White long-sleeved blouse with semi-formal and mess dress uniforms with blue satin inverted V-tie tab with self-fastening tails. Enlisted personnel wear sleeve chevrons only; officers wear shoulder mark insignia. Button epaulets over jumper only when wearing shoulder mark insignia. Military creases are prohibited.

NOTES: **(Pgs 46-47)**
1. Center nametag on right side even to within1 1/2 inches higher or lower than, the first or second button.
2. Center ribbons on left side, horizontal with ground. Bottom of the ribbons is even with bottom of nametag. Ribbons: wear all or none; when ribbons are worn all ribbon devices (*EXAMPLE:* oak leaf) must be worn. See Figure 4.3 for arrangement of ribbons. *EXCEPTIONS:* The Missile Badge and Excellence-In-Competition badge is worn 1 1/2 inches below bottom of ribbons and centered or on the right side 1/2 inch above nametag.
3. Air Force members are highly encouraged to wear their current occupational badge. Aeronautical and chaplain badges are mandatory, others are optional. Center aeronautical, occupational,

or miscellaneous badge 1/2 inch above the ribbons. When not wearing ribbons, center parallel to the nametag. Center additional badge 1/2 inch above first one. Center duty or miscellaneous badge on the right side centered 1/2 inch above the nametag. If placing duty or miscellaneous badges above the nametag, center an additional badge 1/2 inch above the first one. The Missile Badge and Excellence-In-Competition badge is worn 1 1/2 inches below bottom of ribbons and centered or on the right side 1/2 inch above nametag.

4. Center duty or miscellaneous badge 1/2 inch above nametag.

5. Air Force Command Insignia: Current commander center 1/2 inch above nametag; graduated commander center 1/2 inch below nametag. If duty badges are worn they will be worn 1/2 inch above command insignia (current commander). AF Command insignia is mandatory.

6. Officers place shoulder mark insignia as close as possible to shoulder seam. Airmen center 3 1/2 inch sleeve chevron halfway between shoulder seam and bottom of sleeve. Senior NCOs wear shoulder mark insignia or chevrons.

7. Tie tab is optional with short-sleeved blouse.

NOTES: **(Pgs 41-42)**
1. Center metallic nametag on right side even to within 1 1/2 inches higher or lower than the first exposed button
2. Center ribbons on left side parallel with ground. Align bottom of the ribbons with the bottom of the nametag. Ribbons are mandatory. When ribbons are worn all ribbons and devices must be worn. See Figure 4.3 for arrangement of ribbons.
3. Air Force members are highly encouraged to wear their current occupational badge. Aeronautical and chaplain badges are mandatory, others are optional. Wear only mid-size or regular badges, do not mix sizes. Center aeronautical, occupational, or miscellaneous badge 1/2 inch above the top row of ribbons. Center additional badge 1/2 inch above first one Center aeronautical, occupational, or miscellaneous badge 1/2 inch above the ribbons. When not wearing ribbons, center badge parallel to the nametag. Center additional badge 1/2 inch above first one. Center duty or miscellaneous badge on the right side centered 1/2 inch above the nametag. If placing duty or miscellaneous badges above the nametag, center an additional badge 1/2 inch above the first one.
EXCEPTIONS: The Missile Badge and Excellence-In-

Competition badge is worn 1 1/2 inches below bottom of ribbons and centered or on the right side 1/2 inch above nametag.

4. Air Force Command Insignia: Current commander center 1/2 inch above nametag; graduated commander center 1/2 inch below nametag. If duty badges are worn they will be worn 1/2 inch above command insignia (current commander). AF Command insignia is mandatory.

5. Officers place shoulder mark insignia as close as possible to shoulder seam; button epaulets of blouse over jumper. Enlisted personnel center 3 1/2 inch sleeve chevron halfway between shoulder seam and elbow bent at 90-degree angle. Senior noncommissioned officers may wear sleeve chevrons or epaulets.

6. Tie tab is mandatory.

7. Long-sleeved shirt is mandatory.

Maternity Mess Dress Uniform, Figure 2.20, (Pg 43)

NOTES: **(Pg 43)**

1. Nametag and headgear is not worn. Saluting is required when outdoors.

2. Air Force members are highly encouraged to wear their current occupational badge. Aeronautical and chaplain badges are mandatory, others are optional. Wear only mid-size or regular badges, do not mix sizes. Center aeronautical, occupational, or miscellaneous badge 1/2 inch above medals. Center additional badge 1/2 inch above first one. Center duty or miscellaneous badge on right side with bottom edge of badge parallel to top of medals or comparable position when not authorized medals; this includes Missile and Excellence-In-Competition badges. If placing duty or miscellaneous badges on the right side, center an additional badge 1/2 inch above the first one.

3. Air Force Command Insignia: Worn on the right side of the uniform in the same relative position as badges worn on the left and (if applicable) miscellaneous or duty badge will be 1/2 inch above command insignia. AF Command Insignia is mandatory.

4. Center all miniature medals on left side even to within 1 1/2 inches higher or lower than the first exposed button, horizontal with the ground. See Figure 4.2 for arrangement of medals.

5. Officers place shoulder mark insignia as close as possible to shoulder seam; button epaulets of blouse over jumper. Enlisted personnel center 3 1/2 inch sleeve chevron halfway between shoulder seam and elbow bent at 90-degree angle. Senior noncommissioned officers wear sleeve chevrons only.

6. Tie tab is mandatory.

7. Wear white long-sleeved blouse with mess dress uniform with blue satin inverted V-tie tab.

Women's Semi-Formal Dress (Maternity-Enlisted Only), Figure 2.21, (Pg 44)

NOTES: (Pg 44)

1. Nametag and headgear is not worn. Saluting is required when outdoors.

2. Center ribbons on left side 1 1/2 to 2 1/2 inches below bottom of the tab, horizontal with the ground. Wear all ribbons and devices. See Figure 4.3 for arrangement of ribbons.

3. Air Force members are highly encouraged to wear their current occupational badge. Aeronautical and chaplain badges are mandatory, others are optional. Wear only mid-size or regular badges, do not mix sizes. Center aeronautical, occupational, or miscellaneous badge 1/2 inch above the ribbons. Center additional badge 1/2 inch above first one. Center duty or miscellaneous badge on right side with bottom edge of badge parallel to bottom edge of ribbons, this includes Missile and Excellence-In-Competition. Center duty or miscellaneous badge on the right side centered 1/2 inch above the nametag. If placing duty or miscellaneous badges on the right side, center an additional badge 1/2 inch above the first one.

4. Center 3 1/2 inch sleeve chevron halfway between sleeve and elbow bent at 90-degree angle. Senior noncommissioned officers wear chevrons only.

5. Tie tab is mandatory.

6. Wear white long-sleeved blouse with semi-formal with blue satin inverted V-tie tab.

Jumper (Maternity)

(Maternity Jumper), (Pg 66): Wear with blue maternity blouses with tie tab. Button epaulets of blouse over the jumper only when wearing shoulder mark insignia. Tie tab optional with short-sleeved blouse, mandatory with long-sleeved blouse. Jumper length will be no shorter than the top of the kneecap nor longer than the bottom of the kneecap.

(Maternity Jumper, Mess Dress, Semi-Formal), (Pg 67): Wear with white, long-sleeved maternity blouse only. Enlisted personnel wear sleeve chevrons only; officers wear shoulder mark insignia. Button epaulets over jumper only when wearing shoulder mark insignia. *NOTE:* Miniature medals are worn instead of ribbons, if worn in place of the mess dress uniform; ribbons are worn with semi-formal uniform.

NOTES: **(Pgs 45-46)**
1. Center plastic blue laminated nametag on right side even to within 1 1/2 inches higher or lower than the first exposed button.
2. Ribbons are optional. If worn, all ribbons and devices will be worn. Center ribbons on left side, horizontal with ground. Bottom of the ribbons is even with bottom of nametag. See Figure 4.3 for arrangement of ribbons.
3. Air Force members are highly encouraged to wear their current occupational badge. Aeronautical and chaplain badges are mandatory, others are optional. Wear only mid-size or regular size badges, do not mix sizes. Center aeronautical, occupational, or miscellaneous badge 1/2 inch above the top row of ribbons. Center additional badge 1/2 inch above first one. Center duty or miscellaneous badge on the right side centered 1/2 inch above the nametag. If placing duty or miscellaneous badges above the nametag, center an additional badge 1/2 inch above the first one. The Missile Badge and Excellence-In-Competition badge is worn 1 1/2 inches below bottom of ribbons and centered or on the right side 1/2 inch above nametag.
4. Air Force Command Insignia: Current commanders wear the insignia centered 1/2 inch above the nametag. Graduated commanders, when worn, wear the insignia centered 1/2 inch below the nametag. AF Command Insignia is mandatory.
5. Officers place shoulder mark insignia as close as possible to shoulder seam; button epaulets of blouse over jumper. Enlisted short-sleeved shirt, center 3 1/2 inch sleeve chevron halfway between shoulder seam and bottom of sleeve. Long-sleeved: 3 1/2 inch sleeve chevron halfway between sleeve and elbow bent at 90-degree angle. Senior NCOs wear shoulder mark insignia or chevrons. Button epaulets of blouse over jumper only when wearing shoulder marks.
6. Tie tab is mandatory with long-sleeved blouse, optional with short-sleeved blouse.

Maternity Skirt (Maternity Service Dress, Long-Sleeved Maternity Blouse, Short-Sleeved Maternity Blouse), (Pg 68):
Polyester serge with expansion panel.

Slacks (Maternity) (Maternity Service Dress, Long-Sleeved Maternity Blouse, Short-Sleeved Maternity Blouse, (Pg 67): Polyester serge with expansion panel.

Women's Maternity Battle Dress Uniform (BDU), Figure 2.8, (Pg 27)

NOTES: (Pgs 27-28)

1. Center U.S. AIR FORCE tape on left side of BDU shirt and same relatively position as on regular BDU shirt. Center nametape *(last name only)* on the right side of the BDU shirt and same relatively position as on the regular BDU shirt. Cut or fold tapes to match pocket width. Maternity BDU: Place in same relative position.

2. Air Force members are highly encouraged to wear their current occupational badge. Aeronautical and chaplain badges are mandatory, others are optional. Center subdued embroidered badge (aeronautical, occupational, or miscellaneous) 1/2 inch above U.S. AIR FORCE tape. Center additional badge 1/2 inch above the first badge. A third badge (duty or miscellaneous) may be worn on lower portion of left pocket between left and right edges and bottom of flap and bottom of pocket, this includes Missile and Excellence-In-Competition badges.

3. Air Force Command Insignia: The subdued cloth insignia will be centered 1/2 inch above the nametape for current commanders or centered on the right pocket flap below the nametape for graduated commanders. AF Command insignia is mandatory. Badges/patches will be worn 1/2 inch above insignia (current commanders).

4. (MAJCOM/FOA/DRU Commanders' discretion). Center subdued organizational patch (MAJCOM/wing/squadron) on lower portion of (from right to left) pockets between the left and right edges and bottom of flap and pocket. When prescribed, center additional patch over right pocket 1/2 inch above nametape. Maternity BDU: Place emblems and badges in same relative position. *NOTE*: Personnel attached to Army units may wear associate unit patch, only while attached to the unit.

5. Generals wear 1 inch blue subdued cloth aligned (point-to-point) or subdued metal pin-on grade insignia. 3/4 inch stars are optional if unable to wear the 1 inch blue subdued cloth aligned (point-to-point) or subdued metal pin-on grade insignia. All other officers: center regular size subdued cloth or subdued metal pin-on grade insignia. Enlisted personnel: center 3 1/2 or 4 inch (women) or 4 inch (men) sleeve chevron halfway between shoulder seam and elbow when bent at 90-degree angle (when sleeves are rolled up, chevrons do not need to be fully visible, but must be distinguishable). Refer to Figure 2.9 for placement of officer grade insignia.

6. Individuals may sew down pockets but no local policy will be established to make it mandatory.

(Maternity Battle Dress), (Pg 81): Cotton and nylon twill or rip stop cotton with a front stretch panel with elastic waistband, side pockets with flaps on both legs, and six pockets. Material of shirt and slacks must match. May or may not be bloused. If not bloused, tie straps will be removed and trousers will be ankle length and hang naturally, barely resting on the boot without a break in the crease.

Other (Maternity Battle Dress, Battle Dress Uniform), (Pg 85):

MAJCOM or Installation Commanders prescribe other functional clothing usually worn with BDUs and list them in a supplement to this instruction.

Joint Task Force Commanders prescribe the wear of the U.S. flag as red, white, and blue; subdued colored flags are not authorized. Flag worn on left shoulder; approximately 2 x 3 inches and placed with star field to face forward or the flag's own right. The appropriate replica for the right shoulder sleeve is identified as the reverse side flag. Flag is not worn in the CONUS.

Women's Service and Dress Uniforms (see notes), Table 2.3, (Pgs 60-80)

THIS INCLUDES SERVICE DRESS, MATERNITY SERVICE DRESS, MESS DRESS, FORMAL DRESS AND SEMI-FORMAL DRESS

Accouterments, (Service Dress, Long-Sleeved Shirt, Short-Sleeved Shirt, Maternity Service Dress, Maternity Jumper, Long-Sleeved Maternity Blouse, Short-Sleeved Maternity Blouse, Mess Dress, Formal Dress, Semi-Formal Dress), (Pg 80): Figure of each uniform shows proper placement of accouterments and gives a description of each. The finish of all accouterments must match.

Belt and Buckle, (Service Dress, Long-Sleeved Shirt, Short-Sleeved Shirt, Semi-Formal Dress), (Pg 68): With skirt or slacks with belt loops; silver-tip end of the belt extends beyond the buckle facing the wearer's right; no blue fabric shows.

Cufflinks
(Service Dress, Long-Sleeved Blouse, Maternity Jumper, Long-Sleeved Maternity Blouse, Semi-Formal), (Pg 78): "wing and star" design; satin finish with AF symbol; or plain silver highly polished, cufflinks. Optional with all uniforms.

Studs (Mess Dress), (Pg 78): Plain silver highly polished or satin finished to match cufflinks.

Cummerbund (Mess Dress, Formal Dress), (Pg 69): Worn with open edge of pleats facing up; blue satin with mess dress, silver with formal dress.

Earmuffs (Service Dress, Maternity Service Dress, Mess Dress, Formal, Semi-Formal), (Pg 78): (commercial design of any material). Wear only with authorized outergarments and service dress uniform.

Footwear

Combat Boots (Black/Jungle Boot) (Service Dress, Long-Sleeved Shirt, Short-Sleeved Shirt, Long-Sleeved Maternity Blouse, Short-Sleeved Maternity Blouse), (Pg 71): With or without safety toe; must have a plain rounded toe or rounded capped toe with or without perforated seam; zipper or elastic inserts are optional; no designs. Wear with slacks only.

Dress Boots, (Service Dress, Long-Sleeved Shirt, Short-Sleeved Shirt, Maternity Service Dress, Maternity Jumper, Long-Sleeved Maternity Blouse, Short-Sleeved Maternity Blouse), (Pg 69): Heels of a height suitable to the individual but no higher than 2 1/2 inches (measured from inside sole of the boot to end of heel lift). Wear boots with skirt or slacks; however, if worn with skirt, remove boots and wear pumps or oxfords while in work place. Plain, black, commercial design without ornamentation such as buckles, bows, or straps. High-gloss or patent finish optional.

Hose, (Service Dress, Long-Sleeved Shirt, Short-Sleeved Shirt, Maternity Service Dress, Maternity Jumper, Long-Sleeved Maternity Blouse, Short-Sleeved Maternity Blouse, Mess Dress, Formal Dress, Semi-Formal Dress), (Pg 71): Commercial, sheer, nylon in neutral, dark brown, black or off-black, or dark blue shades that complement the uniform and the individual's skin tone. Do not wear patterned hose.

Low Quarters (Black), (Service Dress, Long-Sleeved Shirt, Short-Sleeved Shirt, Maternity Service Dress, Maternity

Jumper, Long-Sleeved Maternity Blouse, Short-Sleeved Maternity Blouse), (Pg 71): Black oxford; lace-up style with a plain rounded toe or a plain rounded capped toe; without design; sole will not exceed 1/2 inch in thickness and the heel will not exceed 1 inch in height (measured from the inside front of the heel); may have low wedge heel. Wear must be plain, black, smooth, scotch-grained leather or man-made material, patent or high-gloss finish, commercial design without ornamentation.

Pumps (Black), (Service Dress, Long-Sleeved Shirt, Short-Sleeved Shirt, Maternity Service Dress, Maternity Jumper, Long-Sleeved Maternity Blouse, Short-Sleeved Maternity Blouse, Mess Dress, Formal, Semi-Formal), (Pg 70): Low cut, rounded throat shoe, with a raised heel no higher than 2 1/2 inches (measured from the inside sole of shoe to the end of heel lift), without fastening. Tip of heel cannot be less than 1/2 inch and no larger than the body of the shoe. Wear must be plain, black, smooth, scotch-grained leather or man-made material, patent or high-gloss finish, commercial design without ornamentation such as, buckles, bows, straps. Black satin optional for mess dress and formal dress. Faddish styles will not be worn (extreme toes -- pointed or squared or extreme heel shapes).

Slip-on Shoes, (Service Dress, Long-Sleeved Shirt, Short-Sleeved Shirt, Maternity Service Dress, Maternity Jumper, Long-Sleeved Maternity Blouse, Short-Sleeved Maternity Blouse),
(Pg 70): Black step-in shoe where the top of the shoe goes over the top of the foot (not mules) with rounded toe or plain rounded capped toe; without design. Wear must be plain, black, smooth, scotch-grained leather or man-made material, patent or high-gloss finish, commercial design without ornamentation such as, buckles, bows, straps. Faddish styles will not be worn (extreme toes -- pointed or squared or extreme heel shapes).

Socks (Black), (Service Dress, Long-Sleeved Shirt, Short-Sleeved Shirt, Maternity Service Dress, Long-Sleeved Maternity Blouse, Short-Sleeved Maternity Blouse), (Pg 71): Plain without design. Plain white socks may be worn with combat boots or dress boots. Wear black socks over white socks to preclude white socks from showing. Wear hose if not wearing socks. Wear only with slacks.

Handbags

Clutch Style (Service Dress, Long-Sleeved Shirt, Short-Sleeved Shirt, Maternity Service Dress, Maternity Jumper, Long-Sleeved Maternity Blouse, Short-Sleeved Maternity Blouse, Mess Dress, Formal, Semi-Formal), (Pg 79): Plain black smooth or scotch-grain leather, patent leather, or high-gloss, or man-made material without ornamentation. Fabric, suede or patent leather with mess dress, formal dress, and ceremonial dress. Purse will be no larger than 6 1/2 x 11 inches or smaller than 5 x 9 inches. It must have a concealed closure and may have a wrist strap. *EXCEPTION:* Do not use patent leather purse when wearing semi-formal dress.

Leather – optional (Service Dress, Long-Sleeved Shirt, Short-Sleeved Shirt, Maternity Service Dress, Maternity Jumper, Long-Sleeved Maternity Blouse, Short-Sleeved Maternity Blouse, Mess Dress, Formal, Semi-Formal), (Pg 79): Plain black leather or vinyl without ornamentation, with or without plain fold-over flap with or without single-placed silver or gold-colored clasp. May have up to two adjustable shoulder straps with or without buckles. May be patent leather or high- gloss not to exceed 13 x 9 x 4 1/2 inches deep.

Shoulder (Service Dress, Long-Sleeved Shirt, Short-Sleeved Shirt, Maternity Service Dress, Maternity Jumper, Long-Sleeved Maternity Blouse, Short-Sleeved Maternity Blouse, Mess Dress, Formal, Semi-Formal), (Pg 79): Plain black leather or vinyl without ornamentation, with or without plain fold-over flap with or without single-placed silver or gold-colored clasp. May have up to two adjustable shoulder straps with or without buckles. May be patent leather or high-gloss not to exceed 13 x 9 x 4 1/2 inches deep.

Headgear

Blue Winter Cap (Service Dress, Maternity Service Dress, Mess Dress, Formal Dress, Semi-Formal Dress), (Pg 77): Only with full-length outergarments, commercial design with ear and neck flaps, ribbon tie or strap with covered metal snap fastener. Do not wear rank insignia.

Flight Cap (Women's), (Service Dress, Long-Sleeved Shirt, Short-Sleeved Shirt, Maternity Service Dress, Maternity Jumper, Long-Sleeved Maternity Blouse, Short-Sleeved Maternity Blouse), (Pg 78): Slightly to the wearer's right with vertical crease of the cap in line with the center of the forehead, in a straight line with the nose; approximately 1 inch from the eyebrows in the front, opening of cap is to the rear; when not wearing, tuck under the belt on either side, between first and second belt loops; cap will not fold over the belt. Cap has dark blue colored edge braid for *Enlisted personnel*, silver-colored edge braid for *General Officers*, and silver and blue in a diamond pattern edge braid for all *other Officers*; all shades and materials are authorized with any uniform combination. See Figure 2.7 for grade insignia placement. Mandatory for all female personnel. Authorized to wear the current men's flight cap.

Service Cap, (Service Dress, Long-Sleeved Shirt, Short-Sleeved Shirt, Maternity Service Dress, Maternity Jumper, Long-Sleeved Maternity Blouse, Short-Sleeved Maternity Blouse), (Pg 77): Squarely on the head; center large size hat insignia on the front of the cap. Rounded design, sides form a front brim, with blue hat cover. Clear plastic rain scarf or white net wind scarf optional; helmet-type designed to cover headgear and tie under chin. *Service cap mandatory for majors and above; optional for all others.*

Watch Cap (Knit), (Black or Navy Blue), (Service Dress, Maternity Service Dress), (Pg 77): Commercial design. Wear when approved by installation commanders and only with authorized outergarments and service dress uniform. Grade insignia is not worn.

Outergarments
General, (Pg 72): Outdoors and removed in an office environment except as noted below. Use good judgment in choosing appropriate garments for wear based on weather conditions and duties. May wear with civilian clothes if grade is

removed. See figure for rank placement. **Ensure bottom of blouse is not visible below the bottom of all outergarments: service dress coat, pullover or cardigan sweaters and lightweight blue jacket.**

Coats

All-Weather Coat (Blue) (Service Dress, Long-Sleeved Shirt, Short-Sleeved Shirt, Maternity Service Dress, Maternity Jumper, Long-Sleeved Maternity Blouse, Short-Sleeved Maternity Blouse, Mess Dress, Formal, Semi-Formal), (Pg 76): Stand-up collar, eight-button front, shoulder epaulets with buttons, sleeve straps with buckles. Water resistant, double- breasted with belt and buckle, button throat closure, shoulder straps, sleeve straps, center back vent, facing tabs, and zip-out liner. Coat will fit loosely enough to accommodate shoulders of a uniform without binding at armholes when arms are moved; sleeves will extend 1/2 inch beyond service coat sleeves; loose fitting with bottom of coat extending to between bottom of knee cap and mid-calf; Coat may be modified from double-breasted to single-breasted during pregnancy; remove all buttons from the front of the garment and instead attach three buttons to the left side front as follows: position the buttons approximately 1 1/2 inches from the left edge of the coat; align the top button with the first buttonhole and sew the other two buttons to align vertically with the top button; belt the coat in the back. Return buttons to original positions following pregnancy. (See note 3) May wear over pullover and cardigan sweaters.

Enlisted:
(Service Dress, Semi-Formal), (Pg 61):
Polyester and wool blend; semi-drape, single-breasted with three buttons, no epaulets, one welt pocket on upper left side, and two lower pocket flaps. With arms hanging naturally, sleeves will end approximately 1/4 inch from the heel of the thumb. Ensure the bottom edge of coat extends 3 to 3 1/2 inches below the top of the thigh; sleeves and lapel will be roll-pressed. Wear 3 1/2 or 4 inch chevron. Coat, skirt and slacks must match in shade and material. Do not wear nametag with Semi-Formal Dress.

(Semi-Formal), (Pg 61): Authorized for enlisted personnel only, same as service dress with matching shade/material skirt. White blouse is worn. Nametag and headgear is not worn.

Lightweight Jacket (Blue) (Long-Sleeved Blouse, Short-Sleeved Blouse, Long-Sleeved Maternity Blouse, Short-Sleeved Maternity Blouse), (Pg 74): Indoor and outdoor garment. Zip up at least halfway; not authorized for wear when service dress uniform is designated or more appropriate. May wear over pullover and cardigan sweaters; however, sweater is not exposed. Partially lined, water repellent, waist length, zipper front, with two slant pockets and knitted cuffs; worn with or without insulated liner. May wear men's style jacket as long as it presents a neat, professional appearance. The AF Symbol may be embroidered on the jacket at member's expense. May not be worn with civilian clothes if the AF symbol is embroidered on the jacket. Women are authorized to wear the men's lightweight blue jacket.

Mess Dress Jacket (Mess Dress), (Pg 62): Worn for social functions of a general or official nature (black tie affairs); an evening gown is civilian equivalent. Single-breasted, loose fitting at the waist with three "wing and star" buttons on each side at front. Jacket ends 2 1/2 to 3 inches below the waistline; front opening will gap approximately 2 to 3 inches at bottom; *General officers* wear 3/4 inch wide silver sleeve braid and all other *Officers wear* 1/2 inch sleeve braid, 2 1/2 inches from end of sleeve; sleeves are wrist length; jacket and skirt match in shade and material. *Mandatory for officers and optional for enlisted.*

Mess Dress Jacket (Officer only), (Formal Dress), (Pg 62): Officers only; for official formal evening functions and state occasions (white tie affairs); evening gown is civilian equivalent.

Officer:

(Service Dress), (Pg 60): Polyester and wool blend; semi-drape, single-breasted with three buttons, epaulets, one welt pocket on upper left side, and two lower pocket flaps. With arms hanging naturally, sleeves will end approximately 1/4 inch from the heel of the thumb. Ensure the bottom edge of coat extends 3 to 3 1/2 inches below the top of the thigh; sleeves and lapel will be roll-pressed. *Colonels* and below wear regular size (1 inch) metal grade insignia on epaulets and 1/2 inch blue sleeve braid 3 inches from end of sleeve. General Officers: Wear 1 inch stars on all uniforms. 3/4 inch stars are optional if unable to wear the 1 inch stars. Wear 1 1/2 inch blue sleeve braid 3 inches from end of sleeve. Coat, skirt and slacks must match in shade and material.

Top Coat (Blue) (Service Dress, Long-Sleeved Shirt, Short-Sleeved Shirt, Maternity Service Dress, Maternity Jumper, Long-Sleeved Maternity Blouse, Short-Sleeved Maternity Blouse, Mess Dress, Formal, Semi-Formal), (Pg 75): Stand-up collar, six-button front, shoulder epaulets with buttons, sleeve straps with buckles. Water resistant, double- breasted with belt and buckle, button throat closure, shoulder straps, sleeve straps, center back vent, facing tabs, and zip-out liner. Coat will fit loosely enough to accommodate shoulders of a uniform without binding at armholes when arms are moved; sleeves will extend 1/2 inch beyond service coat sleeves; loose fitting with bottom of coat extending to between bottom of knee cap and mid-calf; Coat may be modified from double-breasted to single-breasted during pregnancy; remove all buttons from the front of the garment and instead attach three buttons to the left side front as follows: position the buttons approximately 1 1/2 inches from the left edge of the coat; align the top button with the first buttonhole and sew the other two buttons to align vertically with the top button; belt the coat in the back. Return buttons to original positions following pregnancy. (See note 3) May wear over pullover and cardigan sweaters.

Gloves or Mittens (Black) (Service Dress, Maternity Service Dress, Mess Dress, Formal Dress, Semi-Formal), (Pg 77): Leather, knitted, tricot or suede; or a combination of leather, knitted, tricot, and suede.

Scarf (Black) (Service Dress, Maternity Service Dress, Mess Dress, Formal Dress, Semi-Formal), (Pg 77): Tucked in with authorized outergarments. Not authorized with pullover and cardigan sweaters; will not exceed 10 inches in width. All wool or cotton simplex, with or without napped surface.

Sweater

Cardigan Sweater (Blue) (Long-Sleeved Shirt, Short-Sleeved Shirt, Maternity Service Dress, Maternity Jumper, Long-Sleeved Maternity Blouse, Short-Sleeved Maternity Blouse), (Pg 73): 50 percent acrylic and 50 percent non-irritation wool; washable; long-sleeved, with cuffed or uncuffed sleeves; indoor or outdoor garment; buttoned or unbuttoned indoors; must be buttoned outdoors; when buttoned, sweater will be completely buttoned; tie tab is optional; wear collar of shirt inside or outside sweater; not exposed when wearing another outergarment. Hospital personnel do not wear with white uniforms. Maternity may be worn unbuttoned.

Cardigan Sweater (White) (Maternity Jumper, Long-Sleeved Maternity Blouse, Short-Sleeved Maternity Blouse), (Pg 73): White. Worn in a work area or under an outergarment. Maternity may be worn unbuttoned.

Sweater (Pullover) (Long-Sleeved Blouse, Short-Sleeved Blouse), (Pg 72): All wool or wool/acrylic blend, V-neck, long-sleeved, with cuffed sleeves. Indoor or outdoor garment; tie tab is optional; wear collar of blouse inside or outside sweater; not exposed when wearing another outergarment. Place metallic nametag on wearer's right side with the bottom of the nametag level centered between the middle of the sleeve seam and the seam of the neckline; position at an appropriate level down from shoulder seam. Tie and tabs are optional. *NOTE:* Local commanders retain the option to require the wear of a tie or tab with all uniform combinations based on specific circumstances.

Shirt/Blouse

Mess Dress Blouse (White) (Mess Dress, Formal Dress), (Pg 65): Commercial designed, short or long-sleeved with barrel or French cuff; Conventional soft dress-style with turn-down collar with 1/4 inch pleats or 1/8 inch pin tuck pleats. Cufflinks and studs are optional, but must be worn as a set. Worn with blue satin inverted V-tie tab with self-fastening tails. Military creases are prohibited.

Semi-Form Fitting, Long and Short-sleeved Blouse (Blue) (Service Dress, Long-Sleeved Blouse, Short-Sleeved Blouse), (Pg 64): Worn with tie tab when wearing service dress uniform, long-sleeves or when higher decorum is appropriate. Worn with blue inverted V-tie tab with or without self-fastening tails. Same as tuck-in style; princess line, with epaulets and short pointed collar and epaulets; long-sleeves have round cuffs with buttonhole closures on each cuff. **Ensure bottom of blouse is not visible below the bottom of service dress coat, pullover or cardigan sweaters and lightweight blue jacket.** Wear tucked in or out. Long-sleeved blouse may be modified at member's expense to accommodate cufflinks. Military creases are prohibited.

Semi-Form Fitting Blouse (White) (Enlisted Personnel only) (Semi-Formal), (Pg 65): Polyester or cotton, princess line, button-front, with small pointed collar; wear with blue satin inverted V-tie tab with or without self-fastening tails. Military creases are prohibited.

Tuck-in style, Long and Short-Sleeved, (Service Dress, Long-Sleeved Blouse, Short-Sleeved Blouse), (Pg 63): Blue. Worn with tie tab when wearing service dress uniform, long-sleeves or when higher decorum is appropriate. Collar of shirt must show 1/4 to 1/2 inch above coat collar with arms hanging naturally. Long-sleeves extend to heel of thumb; short-sleeves should barely touch or come within 1 inch of the forearm with arms bent at a 90-degree angle; collar lies softly around neck and does not meet in the front, but is separated by blue inverted V-tie tab with self-fastening tails; pointed collar. Long-sleeves have round cuffs with buttonhole closures on each cuff. Blouse may be modified at member's expense to accommodate cufflinks. Will have tapered fit, military creases prohibited on either. Tuck blouse into slacks or skirt.

Skirt

A-line Skirt, (Long-Sleeved Shirt, Short-Sleeved Shirt),

(Pg 68): Modified A-line, six-gore, free hanging, with or without belt loops. Skirt has a left zipper and lining attached to the inside; skirt length will be no shorter than the top of the kneecap nor longer than the bottom of the kneecap.

Polyester Wool, (Service Dress, Long-Sleeved Blouse, Short-Sleeved Blouse, Semi-Formal), (Pg 68): Skirt hangs naturally over the hips with a slight flare; skirt length will be no shorter than the top of the kneecap nor longer than the bottom of the kneecap; straight style with belt loops, a kick pleat in back, two pockets, and a darted front; skirts have a back zipper and lining attached to the waist.

Mess Dress Skirt (Mess Dress, Formal Dress), (Pg 68): Ankle-length (no higher than ankle, no longer than the bottom of the heel), one-panel front, and one-or-two panel back. Straight hanging, with no flare from hip to hem; seam on left side split to top of knee.

Slacks

Slacks (Service Dress, Long-Sleeved Blouse, Short-Sleeved Blouse), (Pg 67): Slacks fit naturally over the hips with no bunching at waist or bagging at seat; bottom front of slack legs rests on the front of shoe or boot with a slight break in the crease; back of legs is approximately 7/8 of an inch longer than the front. Tailored, straight hanging, no flare at bottom, with two one-quarter front pockets and center fly-front opening *or* center front closure with front and back waist darts, two one-quarter top side pockets, and waistband with five belt loops.

Tie Tab

(Service Dress, Long-Sleeved Shirt, Short-Sleeved Shirt, Maternity Service Dress, Maternity Jumper, Long-Sleeved Maternity Blouse, Short-Sleeved Maternity Blouse, Semi-Formal), (Pg 69): Blue inverted V-tie tab, polyester herringbone with self-fastening tails.

(Mess Dress), (Pg 69): Blue satin inverted V-tie tab with self-fastening tails.

(Formal Dress), (Pg 69): Attached under collar; silver metallic cloth, lame', crescent-shape, 1 inch wide.

Undergarments (Mandatory) (Service Dress, Long-Sleeved Shirt, Short-Sleeved Shirt, Maternity Service Dress, Maternity Jumper, Long-Sleeved Maternity Blouse, Short-Sleeved Maternity Blouse, Mess Dress, Formal, Semi-Formal), (Pg 80): Bra and panties with all uniforms; wear other appropriate undergarments as necessary, provided they are not visible at the neck when worn with an open collar; may wear the white crew-neck style undershirt when wearing closed collar service and dress uniforms. Undershirt will be tucked into slacks or skirt.

NOTES: **(Pg 80)**
1. The mess dress is optional for enlisted personnel and mandatory for officers. Only officers wear the formal dress. Only enlisted personnel wear the semi-formal dress.
2. Enlisted personnel receive a supplementary clothing allowance according to AFI 36-3014 for maternity uniforms. Officers and enlisted personnel begin wearing the maternity uniform when wear of other service uniforms is impractical. Maternity uniform may be worn for up to 6 months after delivery. Officers and enlisted personnel wear the maternity service dress coat or jumper with white blouse and blue satin polyester herringbone twill tie tab when attending functions requiring dress uniforms.

3. Commanders may recommend the following outergarments for pregnant women (1st choice – blue overcoat (move buttons over) - 2nd choice parka - 3rd choice Gortex)

When to Wear Battle Dress, Table 2.2, (Pg 92)

Members will wear Battle Dress when they: Travel on Air Mobility Command (AMC) aircraft during intra-theater deployments and the command directs. (BDU & DCU only)

Members will not wear Battle Dress when they: A. Eat in restaurants where most other diners wear business attire. **B.** Go to establishments that operate primarily to serve alcohol. **C.** Attending off-duty education conducted off a military installation.

Members have the option to wear Battle Dress when they: A. Eat at local establishments where people wear comparable civilian attire. **B.** Make short convenience stops (including shopping malls). **C:** Deploy to perform emergency or periodic maintenance and do not traverse commercial airports. (BDU only)

NOTES: (Pg 26)

1. Center U.S. AIR FORCE tape immediately above left breast pocket. Center nametape *(last name only)* immediately above right breast pocket. Cut or fold tapes to match pocket width.

2. Air Force members are highly encouraged to wear their current occupational badge. Aeronautical and chaplain badges are mandatory, others are optional. Center subdued embroidered badge (aeronautical, occupational, or miscellaneous) 1/2 inch above U.S. AIR FORCE tape. Center additional badge 1/2 inch above the first badge. A third badge (duty or miscellaneous) may be worn on lower portion of left pocket between left and right edges and bottom of flap and bottom of pocket, this includes Missile and Excellence-In-Competition badges.

3. Air Force Command Insignia: The subdued cloth insignia will be centered 1/2 inch above the nametape for current commanders or centered on the right pocket flap below the nametape for

71

graduated commanders. AF Command insignia is mandatory. Badges/patches will be worn 1/2 inch above insignia for current commanders.

4. (MAJCOM/FOA/DRU Commanders' discretion). Center subdued organizational patch (MAJCOM/wing/squadron) on lower portion of (from right to left) pockets between the left and right edges and bottom of flap and pocket. When prescribed, center additional patch over right pocket 1/2 inch above nametape. *NOTE*: Personnel attached to Army units may wear associate unit patch, only while attached to the unit.

5. Generals wear 1 inch blue subdued cloth aligned (point-to-point) or subdued metal pin-on grade insignia. 3/4 inch stars are optional if unable to wear the 1 inch blue subdued cloth aligned (point-to-point) or subdued metal pin-on grade insignia. All other officers: center regular size subdued cloth or subdued metal pin-on grade insignia. Enlisted personnel: center 3 1/2 or 4 inch (women) or 4 inch (men) sleeve chevron halfway between shoulder seam and elbow when bent at 90-degree angle (when sleeves are rolled up, chevrons do not need to be fully visible, but must be distinguishable). Refer to Figure 2.9 for placement of officer grade insignia.

6. Individuals may sew down pockets but no local policy will be established to make it mandatory. Secure BDU pant legs around or in the uppermost portion of combat boot so the fabric of the lower exposed pant leg blouses over the top edge of the combat boot.

Men's Battle Dress Uniform, Table 2.2, (Pg 56)

Belt and Buckle, (Pg 56): Black tip of belt may extend up to 2 inches beyond the buckle facing the wearer's left; blue woven cotton web or elastic with black metal tip and matching buckle. Black web or black riggers belt with nondescript black buckle authorized as an optional item with BDU.

Earmuffs, (Black), (Pg 58): Black (commercial design of any material). With outergarments only and service dress uniform.

Footwear, (Combat Boots) (Black/Jungle Boot), (Pg 56): Black, with or without safety toe, plain rounded toe or rounded capped toe with or without perforated seam. Zipper or elastic inserts optional, smooth or scotch-grained leather or man-made material, and may have a high-gloss or patent finish, optional.

Gloves or Mittens (Black), (Pg 58): With outergarments only. *EXCEPTION:* May wear with BDU without outergarments; leather, knitted, tricot or suede, or a combination of leather, knitted, tricot, and suede.

Headgear

> **(BDU Cap) Mandatory, (Pg 56):** Squarely on the head with no hair protruding in front of the cap; when not being worn, may be stowed in either of the lower cargo pockets on the trousers. BDU caps required for all deployments, field training, mobility exercises and recalls. Hat may not be pushed, rolled, folded or tucked in. (e.g., Ranger Fold) Plain without design.

> **Organizational Baseball Cap, (Pg 57):** The organizational commander must request installation commander's approval to wear an organizational baseball cap (initial request or request for change). These caps are to be worn at squadron level and above only; they are not authorized for wear while in uniform by organizations below squadron level (e.g., Honor Guard, Prime Beef, etc.). They are to be worn in and around the local area of the members' permanent duty location and may be worn on CONUS and OCONUS TDY's when not in a combat area or in support of a contingency. The installation commander prescribes wear of the organizational baseball cap during local exercises and contingencies. When authorized by the installation commander, wear the baseball cap with the BDU; it is not to be worn with the all-weather coat, overcoat, raincoat, or lightweight jacket. Installation commanders prescribe the color, unit designation, and cloth or silkscreen organization emblem, or cloth or silkscreen badge to be worn on the front of the cap, centered above visor. Caps may contain both organizational lettering, numbering, and badge or emblem. Modest shadowing of contrasting colors to delineate organizational lettering and numbering on the front

crown area may contain white and no more than two other colors (excluding patch). Clouds and darts are authorized for Majors and above on the bill of the cap. No other features such as stars, designs, individual's name, are authorized. Officer grade insignia is required. When worn, officers will wear regular size (1 inch) subdued or non-subdued metal grade insignia centered above visor. Enlisted personnel do not wear grade insignia. When not worn, the cap may be attached to either lower cargo pocket on the BDU trousers.

Watch Cap, (Knit) (Black or Navy Blue), (Pg 57): Commercial design. Wear when approved by installation commanders and only with authorized outergarments and service dress uniform. Grade insignia is not worn.

Outergarments
General, (Pg 57): Worn outdoors only, removed in an office environment, except as noted below. Use good judgment in choosing appropriate garments for wear based on weather conditions and duties. May wear with civilian clothes if all accoutrements (rank, nametapes, patches, etc.) are removed. See Figure 2.9. for grade insignia placement.

Coats:
Camouflage Field Jacket, (Pg 58): Configure accouterments on jacket the same as the BDUs except officers wear subdued cloth or metal grade insignia on the epaulets.

Woodland Patterned (Gortex Parka and Pants), (Pg 58): (Optional item) Gortex Parka and Pants, cold weather. Nylon lining, nylon inner and outer layer, plastic intermediate layer, knitted inner layer, taffeta lining with plain weave outer layer. Printed camouflage. Jacket hood may be stowed in neck collar area. *Enlisted personnel* wear slide-on subdued grade insignia; *officers* wear slide-on or pin-on subdued grade insignia. **NOTE:** Gortex liner will not be worn as an outergarment. Individuals may wear the Gortex parka and pants while performing duties in inclement weather. Parka may be worn without the Gortex pants; however Gortex pants must be worn with parka. (See Chapter 3)

All-Weather Coat (Blue Double-Breasted), (Pg 58):
Stand-up collar, six-button front, shoulder epaulets with buttons, sleeve straps with buckles, split raglan and set in the back. Coat will fit loosely enough to accommodate shoulders of an uniform without binding at armholes when arms are moved; sleeves will extend 1/2 inch beyond service coat sleeves; length of coat will fall between knee length to 6 inches below back crease of knee; top button may be left unbuttoned; fly front, with zip-out liner, slash-through pockets, center vent.

Scarf, (Pg 58): Tucked in with authorized outergarments. Will not exceed 10 inches in width; all wool or cotton simplex, with or without napped surface.

Socks, (Pg 56): Plain without design. Plain white socks may be worn with combat boots. Wear black socks over the white socks to preclude white socks from showing.

Shirt (Long-Sleeved), (Pg 56): Long-sleeved camouflage pattern may be rolled up; if rolled up, sleeve material must match shirt and will touch or come within 1 inch of forearms when arm is bent at 90-degree angle. Ensure chevron is *partially visible*; shirt may be removed in the immediate work area. When removed, T-shirt (other than the athletic or sleeveless style) will be worn. Cotton and nylon twill or rip stop cotton; single-breasted with four bellow pockets with flaps; straight-cut bottom sleeve tabs, and side body panels with or without take-up tabs. Military creases are prohibited.

Trousers, (Pg 56): Cotton and nylon twill or rip stop cotton with button front closure, strap ankle adjustment, and six pockets. Blouse trousers over combat boots or tuck trousers into boots to give a bloused effect. Blousing is defined as: to gather in and drape loosely (cannot be folded or have a tapered look). Material of shirt and trousers must match.

Undergarments, (Pg 58): Mandatory.

Undershirt, (Pg 59): Brown or black. Either V-neck, U-neck, crew-neck, or athletic style without pockets. Undershirt will be tucked into trousers. *EXCEPTION: MAJCOM commanders* may approve black, crew-neck undershirts, long-sleeved black or brown turtlenecks, dickies, or thermal undershirt without pockets. Members may wear white thermal undershirts even if exposed at neck. *Installation commanders* may prescribe unit designation, and cloth or silkscreen emblem to be worn on left side of chest not to exceed 5 inches in diameter.

Other, (Pg 59)

MAJCOM or Installation Commanders may prescribe other functional clothing usually worn with BDUs and list them in a supplement.

Joint Task Force Commanders may prescribe the wear of the U.S. flag as red, white, and blue: subdued colored flags are not authorized. Flag approximately 2 x 3 inches worn on left shoulder and placed with star field to face forward or the flags own right. The appropriate replica for the right shoulder sleeve is identified as the reverse-side flag. Flag is not worn while assigned in the CONUS.

Women's Battle Dress Uniforms, Table 2.4, (Pg 81)

Belt and Buckle (Battle Dress Uniform), (Pg 81): Black tip of belt may extend up to 2 inches beyond the buckle facing the wearer's left or right; blue woven cotton web or elastic with black metal tip and matching buckle. Black web or black riggers belt with nondescript black buckle authorized as an optional item with BDU.

Earmuffs (Black) (Maternity Battle Dress, Battle Dress Uniform), (Pg 85): (Commercial design of any material). With outergarments only and service dress uniform.

Footwear
(Combat Boots) (Black/Jungle Boot), (Maternity Battle Dress, Battle Dress Uniform), (Pg 82): Black, with or

without safety toe, plain rounded toe or rounded capped toe with or without safety toe, plain rounded toe or rounded capped toe with or without perforated seam. Zipper or elastic inserts optional, smooth or scotch-grained leather, or man-made material, and may have a high-gloss or patent finish, optional.

Hot Weather, Tropical Boots (Maternity Battle Dress, Battle Dress Uniform), (Pg 82): Green or black cloth or canvas and black leather with plain toe with zipper, or elastic inserts.

Socks (Black) (Maternity Battle Dress, Battle Dress Uniform), (Pg 82): Plain without design. Plain white socks may be worn with combat boots. Wear black socks over the white socks to preclude white socks from showing.

Gloves, (Black)(Maternity Battle Dress, Battle Dress Uniform), (Pg 84): Wear with outergarments only. *EXCEPTION:* May wear with BDU without outergarments; leather, knitted, tricot or suede, or a combination of leather, knitted, tricot, and suede.

Headgear

(BDU Cap) Mandatory, (Maternity Battle Dress, Battle Dress Uniform), (Pg 82): Squarely on the head with no hair protruding in front of the cap; when not being worn, may be stowed in either of the lower cargo pockets on the trousers. BDU caps required for all deployments, field training, and mobility exercises. Hat may not be pushed, rolled, folded or tucked in. (e.g., Ranger Fold)

Organizational Baseball Cap, (Maternity Battle Dress, Battle Dress Uniform), (Pg 83): The organizational commander must request (initial or changes) installation commander's approval to wear an organizational baseball cap. These caps are to be worn at squadron level and above only; they are not authorized for wear while in uniform by organizations below squadron level (e.g., Honor Guard, Prime Beef, etc.). They are to be worn in and around the local area of the members' permanent duty location and may be worn on CONUS and OCONUS TDY's when not in a combat area or in support of a contingency. The installation commander prescribes wear of the organizational baseball cap during local exercises and contingencies. When authorized by the installation commander, wear the baseball cap with the BDU; it is not to be worn with the all-weather coat, overcoat, raincoat, or lightweight jacket. Installation commanders prescribe the color, unit designation, and cloth or silkscreen organization emblem, or cloth or silkscreen badge to be worn on the front of the cap, centered above visor. Caps may contain both organizational lettering, numbering and badge or emblem. Modest shadowing of contrasting colors to delineate organizational lettering and numbering on the front crown may contain white and no more than two other colors (excluding patch). Clouds and darts are authorized for Majors and above on the bill of the cap. No other features such as stars, designs, individual's name, are authorized. Officer grade insignia is required if other grade insignia is visible. When worn, officers will wear regular size subdued or non-subdued metal grade insignia centered above visor. Enlisted personnel do not wear grade insignia. When not worn, the cap may be attached to either lower cargo pocket on the BDU trousers.

Watch Cap (Knit) (Black or Navy Blue) (Maternity Battle Dress, Battle Dress Uniform), (Pg 85): Commercial design. Wear when approved by installation commanders and only with authorized outergarments and service dress uniform. Grade insignia is not worn.

Outergarments

General (Maternity Battle Dress, Battle Dress Uniform), (Pg 83): Worn outdoors only, remove in a work environment, except as noted below. Use good judgment in choosing appropriate garments for wear based on weather conditions and duties. May wear with civilian clothes if grade is removed. See Figure 2.9 for grade insignia placement.

Coats:
Camouflage Field Jacket (Maternity Battle Dress, Battle Dress Uniform), (Pg 84): Configure accouterments the same as the BDUs except officers wear subdued cloth or metal grade insignia on the epaulets.

Woodland Patterned (Gortex Parka and Pants) (Maternity Battle Dress, Battle Dress Uniform), (Pg 84):

(Optional item) Gortex Parka, cold weather. Nylon lining, nylon inner and outer layer, plastic intermediate layer, knitted inner layer, taffeta lining with plain weave outers layer. Printed camouflage. Jacket hood may be stowed in neck collar area. *Enlisted personnel* wear slide-on subdued grade insignia; *officers* wear slide-on or pin-on subdued grade insignia. *NOTE:* Gortex liner will not be worn as an outergarment. Individuals may wear the Gortex parka and pants while performing duties in inclement weather. Parka may be worn without the Gortex pants, however Gortex pants must be worn with parka. (See Chapter 3)

Double-Breasted All-Weather Coat (Maternity Battle Dress, Battle Dress Uniform), (Pg 84): Stand-up collar, six-button front, shoulders epaulets with buttons, sleeve straps with buckles, split raglan and set in the back. Coat will fit loosely enough to accommodate shoulders of BDUs and food service uniform will fit without binding at armholes when arms are moved; sleeves will extend 1/2 inch beyond service coat sleeves; length of coat will fall between knee length to 6 inches below back crease of knee; top button may be left unbuttoned; fly front, with zip-out liner, split raglan sleeves, slash-through pockets, center vents.

Scarf (black) (Maternity Battle Dress, Battle Dress Uniform), (Pg 84): Tucked in with outergarments only, except sweater. Will not exceed 10 inches in width; all wool or cotton simplex, with or without napped surface.

Shirt (Long-Sleeved), (Maternity Battle Dress, Battle Dress Uniform), (Pg 81): Long-sleeved camouflage pattern may be rolled up; if rolled up, sleeve material must match shirt and will touch or come within 1 inch of forearms when arm is bent at 90-degree angle. Ensure chevron is partially *visible*; shirt may be removed in the immediate work area. Cotton and nylon twill or rip top cotton; single-breasted with four bellow pockets with flaps; straight-cut bottom sleeve tabs, and side body panels with or without take-up tabs. Military creases are prohibited.

Trousers

(Battle Dress Uniform), (Pg 81): Cotton and nylon twill or rip stop cotton with button front closure, strap ankle adjustment, and six pockets. Blouse trousers over combat boots. Blousing is defined as: to gather in and drape loosely (cannot be folded or a have a tapered look). Material of shirt and trousers must match.

Undergarments

General (Maternity Battle Dress, Battle Dress Uniform), (Pg 85): Mandatory. See Table 2.3, line 18.

Undershirt (Maternity Battle Dress, Battle Dress Uniform), (Pg 85): Brown or black. V-neck, U-neck, crew-neck, or athletic style or sleeveless style without pockets. Undershirt will be tucked into trousers. *EXCEPTION: MAJCOM commanders* may approve long-sleeved black or brown turtlenecks, dickies, or thermal undershirt. Members may wear white thermal undershirts even if exposed at neck. *Installation commanders* may prescribe unit designation, and cloth or silk screen emblem, to be worn on left side of chest not to exceed 5 inches in diameter. **NOTE**: When worn with maternity uniform, maternity T-shirt is not required to be tucked in.

NOTES: **(Pgs 24-25)**
1. PT shirt may be tucked in or out. May wear short or long-sleeved style AF shirt.
2. Shorts will be worn with T-shirt. The lining in the PT shorts may be removed, however, do not modify the other PT items such as sleeve removal. Spandex shorts and legging (navy blue or black) may be worn under PT shorts (full length leggings may be worn during cold weather periods).
3. Jacket will be worn with T-shirt. Jacket may also be worn as needed.   Jacket, when worn, may be zipped or unzipped. Hood will be stored and zipped when not worn.
4. Pants will be worn with T-shirt Pants do not have to be zipped.
5. Socks (white) will be white in color, any length and may have small conservative trademark logos.
6. Undergarments are mandatory with all PT gear combinations.

7. All hats/winter caps (knit) are authorized. Maintain a professional military image, with no offensive wording, graphics or photos on any item worn with the PT. Bandanas and other similar headscarves/ headgear are not authorized unless due to medical waiver condition.

8. Additional civilian clothing items may be added to the PT, but color consistency should be reasonably compatible to support a professional appearance.

9. Hair standards do not apply while working out with the wear of the PT gear.

10. Tattoos - Body Art (tattoos) and jewelry standards apply (refer to AFI 36-2903, Table 2.5).

11. Saluting is not required.

12. Requirement for the wear of a reflective belt will be at the discretion of the Installation Commander.

13. Jewelry wear will follow normal uniform wear rules; keep safety in mind.

14. Headphones and earphones are authorized while in gym area or designated running track unless prohibited by Installation Commander.

15. Any athletic shoe is authorized.

16. Other issues evolving in the AOR, wear of the PT, will be decided by the AOR Commander.

17. Safety/additional items such as ski wraps/sweatbands (black, blue, white), reflective belts, personal hydration systems, fannypacks, armbands, gloves, etc., are all authorized while performing individual PT.

18. There is no mandated maternity PT while participating in formations, unit activities, similar official events, and when mission/ safety dictates.

19. Local commanders may dictate the wear of the PT gear while performing organized PT.

20. The PT gear can be worn in any combination desired.

21. When participating in organized PT, any combination of the PT gear (shorts, T-shirt, pants and jacket) will be worn as a set and not mixed with civilian clothes; at other times any combination of the PT gear (shorts, T-shirt, pants and jacket) can be worn with civilian clothes. Commanders (or equivalent) will determine which PT events are "organized".

22. For accessions, PME and academic training environments (e.g., USAFA, ROTC, OTS, ASBC, SOS, BMT), PT gear wear is authorized as outlined above; commanders (or equivalent) will determine which PT events are "organized". In these environments, students and staff may wear unit-specific PT gear to meet necessary training requirements (e.g., staff/student distinction, student squadron affiliation, etc.).

<u>**Sweater/Jacket Section**</u>
<u>**Lightweight Blue Jacket, Figure 2.11, (Pg 31)**</u>

NOTES: (Pg 31)
1. May be worn indoors or outdoors and must be zipped at least halfway.
2. May be worn with civilian clothes when insignia is removed.

3. AF Symbol is optional. May be embroidered on the left side at members cost and is not authorized to be worn with civilian clothes.

4. Women may wear the male version of the lightweight blue jacket.

Cardigan Sweater, Figure 2.10, (Pg 30)

NOTES: **(Pg 30)**

1. May be worn indoors or outdoors.

2. Will be buttoned outdoors and or either all buttons fastened or unbuttoned indoors.

3. Tie/Tab is optional.

4. Collar of shirt may be worn inside or outside of sweater.

5. Sleeves may not be worn pushed up.

6. Officers and Senior NCOs wear shoulder mark rank insignia. All other enlisted members wear metal rank insignia 5/8 inch from edge and centered. Center horizontally on the epaulet, with bottom of insignia 1 inch from shoulder seam.

Pullover Sweater, Figure 2.9, (Pg 29)

NOTES: (Pg 29)
1. Place metallic nametag on wearer's right side with the bottom of the nametag level centered between the middle of the sleeve seam and the seam of the neckline; position at an appropriate level down from shoulder seam (applicable to both male and female).
2. May be worn indoors or outdoors.
3. Tie/Tab is optional.
4. Collar of shirt may be worn inside or outside of sweater.
5. Sleeves may not be worn pushed up.
6. Officers and Senior NCOs wear shoulder mark rank insignia. All other enlisted members wear metal rank insignia 5/8 inch from edge and centered. Center horizontally on the epaulet, with bottom of insignia 1 inch from shoulder seam.

7. Sweater may be tucked under as illustrated above.

Organizational Clothing and Equipment, (Pg 94)

Organizational Clothing and Equipment. Organizations issue items listed in AS016. The clothing remains the property of the organization. It meets unique functional or work requirements and includes both distinctive and functional clothing items. Members may sew reflective tape on organizational clothing and equipment or use Velcro on field jackets so they can remove it during contingencies. (Para 3.1, Pg 94)

- See Table 3.1 through Table 3.6 for distinctive clothing items. The tables list only those items that are unique to the uniform and are worn only when performing the duties for which they are issued; they may also be worn traveling to and from official activities. (Para 3.1.1, Pg 94)
- Functional clothing items such as parkas, protective footwear, specialized winter flight clothing will be issued as required. MAJCOM or installation commanders will prescribe wear instructions in supplements to this directive. (Para 3.1.2, Pg 94)

Aircrew Flight Dress Uniforms. MAJCOMs or organizations requiring exception to Flight Dress Uniform (FDU) or aircrew Desert Flight Dress Uniform (DFDU) wear policy should submit Exception to Policy (ETP) request through MAJCOM channels to HQ USAF/A3OT. (OPR: HQ USAF/A3) (Para 3.2, Pg 94)

- General. Personnel authorized wear of the aircrew FDU/DFDU will comply with this instruction, as well as applicable MAJCOM and installation supplements, regardless of AFSC or unit of assignment. (Para 3.2.1, Pg 94)
- The FDU/DFDU is authorized for wear by; personnel assigned to a position identified with Aircrew Position Identifier (API) 1 thru 9 and A thru G (Rated Officers or Career Enlisted Aviators 1AXXX), Rated officers assigned to an API-0 position that are on active aeronautical orders, or those personnel identified as Operations Support/Non-interference flyers currently on active aeronautical orders to perform

inflight aircrew or parachutist duties IAW AFI 11-401, *Aviation Management*, Atch 3, or as authorized in AS016. Additionally, the FDU/DFDU is authorized for wear by personnel in the following Space/Missile Crew AFSCs 13SXA, 13SXB, 13SXC, 13SXD, 13SXE and 1C6XX. Airmen authorized special articles of clothing under an allowance standard will wear the uniform prescribed by the local unit commander and recommended for the type of mission performed. FDUs/DFDUs are authorized functional clothing for those authorized individuals performing flying, parachutist, space and missile crew duties: Flight duty includes preparation, preflight, in-flight, post-flight, and other flight-related duties associated with aircraft operations. Space operations duties will be defined by MAJCOM supplement to this instruction. (Para 3.2.1.1, Pg 94)

- Flight clothing worn by personnel not on aeronautical orders (authorized under AS016) is restricted to flight-related duties. These personnel may not wear flight clothing on days when actual flying is not planned/anticipated. ***EXCEPTION:*** Space/Missile crew FDU/DFDU wear guidance will be outlined in MAJCOM supplements to this instruction. (Para 3.2.1.2, Pg 94)
- The FDU may be worn off base under the same guidelines as the Battle Dress Uniform (BDU). (Para 3.2.1.3, Pg 94)
- The DFDU will not be worn as a day-to-day uniform. MAJCOM or Theater Commanders may authorize DFDU to be worn during contingencies, exercises, deployments, and tactical training requiring desert camouflage as appropriate for climatic conditions. (Para 3.2.1.4, Pg 94)
- Organizational/Installation commanders may prescribe further limits on the wear of FDUs based on mission requirements and in the interest of morale, health, and welfare of their personnel. (Para 3.2.1.5, Pg 95)
- Morale patches are not authorized for wear. Morale patches include, but are not limited to specialty, competition, or recognition patches (except as noted in paragraphs 3.2.5.4, 3.2.5.6 and 3.2.5.7). (Para 3.2.1.6, Pg 95)
- FDU/DFDUs and Jackets will be maintained IAW T.O.

14P3-1-112, *Maintenance Instructions Nomex Flight Gear, Coveralls, Gloves, Jacket and* AFI 11-301V1, *Aircrew Life Support (ALS) Program,* Chapter 6, *Aircrew Clothing and Equipment.* (Para 3.2.1.7, Pg 95)

Flight Duty Uniform. The FDU/DFDU will have sleeves rolled down to the wrist at all times. The front zipper of the FDU/DFDU will be closed to approximately 3 inches from the neckline. All other zippers will be completely closed. ***EXCEPTION:*** The flight cap may be stored in either lower leg pocket without that pocket being fully zipped. A small portion of the cap may be exposed while in the pocket. However, when the cap is removed, the pocket must be fully zipped. (Para 3.2.2, Pg 95)

- For HQ staff personnel, members may wear the FDU/DFDU configured as directed by DCS or equivalent. (Para 3.2.2.1, Pg 95)
- Velcro fasteners should normally be (green/tan) in color with a 2 x 4 inch rectangular piece of Velcro on the left breast of the FDU/DFDU for placement of the nametag. Center a Velcro silhouette of the MAJCOM or equivalent emblem on the right breast of the FDU/DFDU, above the right breast pocket. Velcro for shoulder patches will be 3 ½ inches square. (Para 3.2.2.2, Pg 95)
- The pen pocket flap located on the left sleeve may be removed unless prohibited by MAJCOM Supplement or restricted due to safety of flight concerns. (Para 3.2.2.3, Pg 95)
- Cell phone/pager/personal digital assistant will be worn IAW Table 2.6 (item 10) *Clothing/Accessory Standards.* (Para 3.2.2.4, Pg 95)

Flight Jacket. The Installation commander determines seasonal requirements. Either green Nomex™ or the leather A-2 flying jacket may be worn with the FDU. The desert style Nomex™ or the leather A-2 flying jacket may be worn with the DFDU. Jackets are required to be zipped at least halfway. Accouterments on the Nomex™ jacket will be configured the same as the FDU/DFDU. (Para 3.2.3, Pg 95)

- Leather A-2 Flying Jacket is authorized for wear as prescribed in Table 3.6 of this instruction. Wear of the leather A-2 jacket in flight is authorized unless prohibited by MAJCOM Supplement or restricted due to safety of flight concerns. Authorized individuals are listed below. (Para 3.2.3.1, Pg 95)

- Aircrew Members. Rated, Career Enlisted Aviators, and Non-rated Aircrew members who have been permanently awarded an aeronautical badge IAW 11-402. The aeronautical order permanently awarding the aeronautical badge constitutes authority for wear of the leather A-2 flying jacket. (Para 3.2.3.1.1, Pg 95)

- Space and Missile Officer/Enlisted. Qualified 13SX officers are authorized wear upon completion of qualification training in one of the following AFSCs 13SXA, 13SXB, 13SXC, 13SXD, 13SXE. Space Systems Operations personnel must complete qualification training and be certified as a mission ready crewmember in the 1C6XX AFSC. (Para 3.2.3.1.2, Pg 95)

EXCEPTION: CSAF is the approval/waiver authority for issue of the leather A-2 flying jacket to all other individuals.

- Gortex Parka and Pants are authorized for wear with the FDU/DFDU while performing ground duties. Individuals may wear the Gortex parka and pants while performing duties in inclement weather. Parka may be worn without the Gortex pants, however Gortex pants must be worn with parka. Gortex is not authorized for wear in flight by aircrew members. These items will be worn IAW Table 2.2, Line 7, of this instruction. (Para 3.2.3.2, Pg 96)

- Nomex™ flight jackets may not be worn with service uniforms. (Para 3.2.3.3, Pg 96)

Headgear. Flight cap is worn with the FDU as described in Chapter 2 of this instruction. Headgear for the DFDU will be the flight cap, DCU hat, or desert style floppy hat. Headgear is not required while involved in or around aircraft operations. (Para 3.2.4, Pg 96)

- Stocking cap (Watch Cap) is authorized for wear by personnel subject to prolonged exposure to adverse weather only. Color is restricted to black or dark blue. When worn, a jacket must also be worn. (Para 3.2.4.1, Pg 96)
- Organizational baseball caps are not authorized for wear with the FDU/DFDU. EXCEPTION: When approved by MAJCOM/CC, aerial demonstration teams may wear organizational baseball caps while performing demonstration duties. (Para 3.2.4.2, Pg 96)
- Individuals authorized to wear berets in Table 3.6 may wear their berets with the FDU/DFDU. (Para 3.2.4.3, Pg 96)

Accouterments. (Para 3.2.5, Pg 96)
- Grade Insignia. Officers will wear subdued cloth grade insignia on each shoulder of the FDU/DFDU and Nomex™ style flight jackets (Plastic covered grade insignia is not authorized). Grade will be sewn on 5/8 inches from the shoulder seam, centered on the shoulder. Officer grade insignia cloth and cable (thread) standards: FDU base cloth is OG 107, Flag Blue cable #67124 except 2nd LT and Major which are Brown cable #67136; DFDU base cloth is Khaki 2120, Black cable #67138 except 2nd LT and Major which are Brown Cable #67136. Enlisted grade is included on the nametag of the FDU/DFDU and Nomex™style flight jackets. Both officer and enlisted grade insignia on the Leather A-2 Flying Jacket is on the nametag only. (Para 3.2.5.1, Pg 96) **EXCEPTION:** Placement of General Officer (GO) stars on the FDU/DFDU and NOMEX™ jackets will be centered on the shoulder halfway between the neck and shoulder seam. Generals wear 1 inch stars on flight suits; ¾ inch stars may be used if there is insufficient room for the 1 inch stars. GO grade insignia will be on base cloth identified in 3.2.5.1, GO stars will be Flag Blue cable #67124 and displayed point-to-center.
- Nametags. Cloth nametags for FDU/DFDU and Nomex™ style flight jackets will be 2 x 4 inches in size, and worn over the left breast pocket. As a minimum, Aeronautical badge or Space badge (if awarded) are mandatory and

nametags will contain individual's name and grade (grade is only mandatory for enlisted personnel). Embroidered badges will be silver (white) in color. In the case of subdued nametags, embroidered badges will be black or dark blue in color. MAJCOM supplements to this instruction will standardize nametags (i.e., background/border colors, squadron logos, naming convention, etc). Nametags for Leather A-2 Flying Jacket will be 2 x 4 inches, brown or black leather, simulated leather. Emboss with silver wings/badges, first and last name, grade, and USAF. *NOTE:* Commanders authorized to wear the Commanders Badge will wear the badge on the left side of the nametag. The badge will be worn only while performing commander duties. (Para 3.2.5.2, Pg 96)

- Right Breast Pocket. MAJCOM or equivalent emblem will be centered above the right breast pocket. MAJCOM or equivalent emblem for the right breast area of the Leather
- A-2 Flying Jacket will have a brown or black leather, simulated leather background. (Para 3.2.5.3, Pg 97)
- Left Sleeve. Normally the U.S. flag, emblem of appropriate wing, group, or center, positioned no lower than 1 inch from shoulder seam in accordance with MAJCOM supplements to this instruction. Members may wear the Weapons School Patch, USAF Test Pilot School Patch, (graduate or instructor) upon completion of the appropriate school when authorized by MAJCOM supplement to this instruction. If wearing the U.S. flag, it will be red, white, and blue in color portraying a straight flag, not a waving flag. The flag will be approximately 2 x 3 inches, with the union to the front and stripes trailing. Chapter 1, Title 4, United States Code, specifies the flag colors as red, white, and blue; therefore, subdued flag replicas are not authorized for wear on the FDU/DFDU. (Para 3.2.5.4, Pg 97)
- Right Sleeve. The unit emblem (squadron patch) will be worn as authorized through MAJCOM supplement to this instruction. When authorized to fly with another unit, individuals may wear the emblem of the unit they are assigned to for flight duties. (Para 3.2.5.5, Pg 97)

- Add-On Patches. MAJCOMs will publish guidance on wear of add-on patches (i.e., flying hour milestone, instructor, flight examiner scroll, etc). Campaign/exercise patches are not authorized. (Para 3.2.5.6, Pg 97)
- MAJCOM commanders must approve all emblems/patches not specifically addressed in this instruction. (Para 3.2.5.7, Pg 97)
- Neckwear. The wear of scarves will be addressed by MAJCOM supplements. When authorized, scarves will be worn around the neck and tucked in. (Para 3.2.5.8, Pg 97)

Undergarments. Undergarments are required; during flight operations they must be cotton or fire retardant material due to added protection. Undergarments made of 100 percent nylon or polyester are not authorized during flight. Undershirts will be crewneck style and black or brown in color. Wear of any other color undershirt and/or undershirts with pockets is prohibited when wearing the FDU/DFDU. *EXCEPTION:* Commanders may authorize crewmembers to wear a designated unit standardized color undershirt at home station on Fridays. Brown or black colored dickies and turtlenecks are authorized for wear as weather conditions warrant. Thermal undergarments will be black, brown, white, or cream colored and are authorized for wear with the FDU/DFDU as weather conditions warrant. (Para 3.2.6, Pg 97)

Gloves. In-garrison glove wear is IAW Chapter 2, Table 2.2 or Table 2.4 (as applicable). Gloves may be worn with FDU/DFDU without outergarments. Flight Gloves will be worn IAW AFI 11-301V1, Chapter 6, and applicable AFI 11-2(MDS Specific) Volume-3 guidance. (Para 3.2.7, Pg 97)

Footwear. In-garrison, wear any combat boot that is authorized in Chapter 2, Table 2.2 or Table 2.4 (as applicable). Mandatory for flight operations; the primary aircrew boots authorized in AS016, are the FWU-3P, FWU-8/P, and the lightweight model 700, 770, and 790 Bellville® Aircrew Boot. Lace-up zipper inserts may be used. Boots, flying, extreme cold, Sorrel Premium, Mukluks, as well as vapor barrier thermal are authorized for wear during winter flight operations at the discretion of the unit commander. (Para 3.2.8, Pg 97)

Socks. White socks may be worn with boots. During exercises and contingencies, wear black socks, or black socks over the white socks to preclude white socks from showing. Socks should be made of cotton or wool. (Para 3.2.9, Pg 98)

Distinctive Uniforms

- USAF Honor Guard and Arlington National Cemetery Chaplains, Table 3.1, (Pgs 98-99)
- Distinctive Uniforms – Installation and Base Honor Guard, Color Guard, Drill Team, and Military Funeral Detail, Table 3.2, (Pgs 100-101)
- Distinctive Uniforms – The USAF Band, USAF Academy Band, USAF Regional Bands, Table 3.3, (Pgs 101-103)
- Distinctive Uniforms – Security Forces (SF), Table 3.4, (Pg 103)
- Distinctive Uniforms – Office of the Joint Chiefs of Staff Military Security Force, Table 3.5, (Pgs 105-106)
- Distinctive Uniforms – Miscellaneous, Table 3.6, (Pgs 107-109)
- Distinctive Uniforms – Air Force Fitness Center Staff Uniforms, Table 3.7, (Pgs 110-114)
- Distinctive Uniform – Air Force Food Services Uniform, Table 3.8, (Pgs 115-117)
- Distinctive Uniforms – Flight Attendant (FA) Uniform), Table 3.9, (Pgs 118-120) – Figure 3.1 (Dress) (Pg 121) & Figure 3.2 (Flight Attendant Slacks with Vest and Blazer) (Pg 121)
- Distinctive Uniforms – Medical Scrubs (see notes) Table 3.10 (Pg 122)

Awards and Decorations Section

Wear Instructions: Wear regular or miniature size medals and ribbons, except for the Medal of Honor (neck decoration). Do not mix sizes. Do not wear medals and ribbons on outergarments such as all-weather coat, overcoat, and lightweight blue jacket. For order of precedence for awards and decorations, see Figure 4.1. For arrangement of devices and ribbons, see Figure 4.2 and Figure 4.3. For arrangement of medals by rows, see Table 4.1. For arrangement of ribbons on service uniforms, see Table 4.2. For placement of medals on dress coat or jacket, see Table 4.3. Wear only authorized Air Force awards and devices when wearing ribbons and medals. (Para 4.1, Pg 123)

Foreign Decorations: Decorations proffered by foreign governments such as a ribbon, medal device, a badge, sash, sunburst, or neck-type decorations. Air Force Instruction 36-2803, *The Air Force Awards and Decorations Program*, specifies how to accept foreign decorations and the authority required for award acceptance by members. Members must have permission to wear foreign decorations they accept. Wear criteria depends on the type of device the decoration represents. (Para 4.2, Pg 123)

Wear sash, sunburst, or neck-type foreign decorations with the formal dress uniform only, according to the customs of the awarding nation. Wear only one type at a time. (Para 4.2.1, Pg 123)

Wear medals and ribbons on the service uniform, ceremonial uniforms, and semi-formal uniforms when they are the same size as Air Force medals and ribbons. (Para 4.2.2, Pg 123)

Wear badges or miniature medals on the mess dress or formal dress uniform. Wear only one foreign badge. When wearing more than one foreign decoration (miniature medal), wear them in the order earned. (Para 4.2.3, Pg 123)

Non-Air Force Service Awards: Air National Guard (ANG) members wear state decorations when serving in state status but not while on federal active duty. Wear other military service department awards not included in Figure 4.1 in the order the awarding Service prescribes. *EXCEPTION:* Air Force awards take precedence over equal awards. Wear awards for wars, campaigns, and expeditions in the order earned. The Army Valorous Unit and Meritorious Unit Commendation awards are larger than Air Force ribbons. When members wear these awards with their Air Force ribbons, they must purchase ribbons that are the same size as their Air Force ribbons. (Para 4.3, Pg 123)

Wear of Awards and Decorations by Retirees and Honorably Discharged Veterans: Honorably discharged and retired Air Force members may wear full-size or miniature medals on civilian suits on appropriate occasions such as Memorial Day and Armed Forces Day. Female members may wear full-size or miniature medals on equivalent dress. (Para 4.4, Pg 123)

Order of Precedence: Arrange ribbons and medals in the order shown in Figure 4.1. Wear the medal with the highest precedence nearest the lapel on the top row. (Para 4.5, Pg 123) (This book on page 117)

Description of Ribbons: Regular-size ribbons are 1 3/8 x 3/8 inches and miniatures are 11/16 x 3/8 inches. Affix ribbons to the uniform using a detachable, metal and plastic clip-on device. Keep ribbons clean and unfrayed. Ribbons will not have a visible protective coating. (Para 4.6, Pg 123)

Description of Miniature Medals: Miniature medals are 1/2 the size of regular medals. The Medal of Honor is always full size. (Para 4.7, Pg 124)

ORDER OF PRECEDENCE OF AWARDS AND DECORATIONS, Figure 4-1, (pgs 124-127)(See notes 1 - 9)

~Color images on last page~

1. Medal of Honor **2.** Air Force Cross **3.** Distinguished Service Cross **4.** Navy Cross **5.** Defense Distinguished Service Medal **6.** Distinguished Service Medal (See note 1.) **7.** Silver Star **8.** Defense Superior Service Medal **9.** Legion of Merit **10.** Distinguished Flying Cross **11.** Airman's Medal **12.** Soldier's Medal **13.** Navy-Marine Corps Medal **14.** Coast Guard Medal **15.** Bronze Star Medal **16.** Purple Heart **17.** Defense Meritorious Service Medal **18.** Meritorious Service Medal **19.** Air Medal **20.** Aerial Achievement Medal **21.** Joint Service Commendation Medal **22.** Air Force Commendation Medal **23**. Army Commendation Medal **24.** Navy Commendation Medal **25.** Coast Guard Commendation Medal **26.** Joint Service Achievement Medal **27.** Air Force Achievement Medal **28.** Army Achievement Medal **29.** Navy Achievement Medal **30.** Combat Action Ribbon (See note 2.) **31.** Distinguished/Presidential Unit Citation **32.** Navy Presidential Unit Citation **33.** Gallant Unit Citation **34.** Joint Meritorious Unit Citation **35.** Meritorious Unit Award **36.** Air Force Outstanding Unit Award **37.** Air Force Organizational Excellence Award **38.** Prisoner of War Medal **39.** Valorous Unit Award **40.** Navy Unit Commendation **41.** Coast Guard Unit Commendation **42.** Meritorious Unit Commendation (Army/Navy/ Coast Guard) (worn in the order earned) **43.** Navy "E" Ribbon **44.** United States Nonmilitary Decorations (See note 3.) **45.** Combat Readiness Medal **46.** Air Force Good Conduct Medal **47.** Good Conduct Medal **48.** Navy Good Conduct Medal **49.** Marine Corps Good Conduct Medal **50.** Coast Guard Good Conduct Medal **51.** Air Reserve Forces Meritorious Service Medal **52.** Army Reserve Component Achievement Medal **53.** Naval Reserve Meritorious Service **54.** Selected Marine Corps Reserve Medal **55.** Coast Guard Reserve Good Conduct Medal **56.** Outstanding Airman of the Year Ribbon **57.** Air Force Recognition Ribbon **58.** China Service Medal **59.** American Defense Service Medal **60.** Women's Army Corps Service Medal **61.** WWII Theater campaign Medals (See note 4.) **62.** World War II Victory Medal **63.** Occupation Medal (Navy/Army)(worn in the

96

order earned) (See note 5) (See notes 1 - 9) **64.** Medal for Humane Action **65.** National Defense Service Medal **66.** Korean Service Medal **67.** Antarctica Service Medal **68.** Armed Forces Expeditionary Medal **69.** Vietnam Service Medal
70. Southwest Asia Service Medal **71.** Kosovo Campaign Medal **72.** Afghanistan Campaign Medal **73.** Iraq Campaign Medal **74.** Global War on Terrorism Expeditionary Medal **75.** Global War on Terrorism Service Medal **76.** Korean Defense Service Medal **77.** Armed Forces Service Medal **78.** Humanitarian Service Medal **79.** Military Outstanding Volunteer Service Medal **80.** Air and Space Campaign Medal **81.** Air Force Overseas Ribbon (S/L) **82.** Army Overseas Ribbon **83.** Air Force Expeditionary Service Ribbon **84.** Sea Service Deployment Ribbon (Navy and Marine) **85.** Coast Guard Special Operations Service **86.** Coast Guard Sea Service **87.** Air Force Longevity Service Award Ribbon **88.** USAF Basic Military Training Instructor Ribbon **89.** Air Force Recruiter Ribbon **90.** Reserve Medals (Armed Forces/Navy and Marine Corps) (worn in order earned) **91.** NCO Professional Military Education Graduate Ribbon **92.** Army NCO Professional Development Ribbon **93.** USAF BMT Honor Graduate Ribbon **94.** Coast Guard Reserve Honor Graduate Ribbon **95.** Small Arms Expert Marksmanship Ribbon **96.** Navy Pistol Shot Medal (See note 9) **97.** Air Force Training Ribbon **98.** Army Service Ribbon **99.** Philippine Defense Ribbon **100.** Philippine Liberation Ribbon **101.** Philippine Independence Ribbon **102.** Merchant Marine Combat Bar **103.** Merchant Marine War Zone (worn in order earned) **104.** Foreign Decorations (See note 6) **105.** Philippine Presidential Unit Citation **106.** Republic of Korea Presidential Unit Citation
107. Other Foreign Unit Citations (See note 6.) **108.** United Nations Service Medal **109.** United Nations Medal **110.** NATO Medal **111.** Multilateral Organization Awards (See note 8.) **112.** Republic of Vietnam Campaign Medal **113.** Kuwait Liberation Medal (Kingdom of Saudi Arabia) **114.** Kuwaiti Liberation Medal (Government of Kuwait) **115.** Republic of Korea War Service Medal **116.** Foreign Service Medals (See note 7)

NOTES: **(Pg 127)**

1. Wear the Air Force Distinguished Service Medal (DSM) ahead of a Distinguished Service Medal awarded by the Army, Navy, and Coast Guard.

2. Awarded only by the Navy, Marine Corps and Coast Guard.

3. A few of the decorations awarded by federal agencies are: Medal of Merit, National Security Medal, Presidential Medal of Freedom, Medal of Freedom, Gold and Silver Lifesaving Medals, NASA Distinguished Service Medal, Public Health Service Decorations (Distinguished Service Medal, Meritorious Service Medal, and Commendation Medal); U.S. Maritime Service Decorations (Distinguished Service Medal, Meritorious Service Medal, and Mariner's Medal). Do not wear these decorations unless you wear U.S. military decorations and service medals. If you wear more than one, arrange them in the order of acceptance. If you wear two or more from the same agency, that agency decides the precedence. Ribbons must be the same size as Air Force ribbons. Wear only those decoration ribbons awarded by federal agencies and earned while in military service.

4. The American Campaign Medal, Asiatic-Pacific Campaign Medal, and European-African-Middle Eastern Campaign Medal are World War II Theater Campaign Medals. If authorized more than one, wear them in the order earned.

5. When awarded more than one clasp, wear in the order earned on the suspension ribbon. Do not wear clasps on the service ribbon.

6. Do not wear these decorations unless you wear other U.S. military decorations and service medals. When authorized more than one, wear them in the order earned. If authorized more than one from the same foreign country, wear them in the order the country prescribes. On special occasions and as a matter of courtesy to a given country, you may wear the decorations of that country ahead of all other foreign decoration

7. Before you wear Foreign Service ribbons, meet conditions in AFI 36-2803. When authorized to wear more than one, wear them in the order earned.

8. Includes ribbons such as: Multinational Force Observers Medal and Inter-American Defense Board Medal. Wear these ribbons in

the order earned and ensure they are the same size as Air Force
ribbons.

9. Only personnel who have served in the U.S. Navy are authorized
to wear either the Navy Expert Rifle or Navy Expert Pistol Shot
Ribbon/Medal

Placement of Devices on Ribbons and Medals, Figure 4.2, _(Pg 128)_

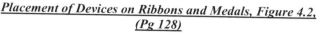

SEPARATE DEVICES:

(SILVER DEVICES ARE PLACED TO THE WEARER'S RIGHT OF BRONZE DEVICES.)

SINGLE CONSTRUCTION:

SINGLE
CONSTRUCTION:

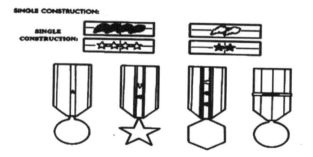

NOTES: (Pgs 128-129)
1. Wear a maximum of four devices on each ribbon. Place silver
devices to the wearer's right of bronze devices. Replace the bronze
device with a silver device after receipt of the fifth bronze device.
Place clusters horizontally and tilt slightly downward to the
wearer's right to allow maximum number of clusters and other
devices on the ribbon. Tilt all or none.

2. On medals, place clusters vertically with silver clusters and stars above similar bronze devices.

3. If all authorized devices do not fit on a single ribbon, wear a second ribbon. Wear a minimum of 3 devices on the first ribbon before wearing a second ribbon. When wearing the second ribbon, place after the initial ribbon. It counts for one award. When future awards reduce devices to a single ribbon, remove the second ribbon.

4. Wear regular devices on regular medals and regular ribbons; miniature devices on miniature ribbons and medals. Wear all the same size devices.

5. There are two methods of affixing devices on ribbons: a separate device or single-constructed device (2 or more devices manufactured together). When affixing separate devices to the ribbon, space devices equally. If using single-constructed device, center it. If using single-constructed device on one ribbon, use it on all ribbons. Place silver clusters, stars, etc., above similar bronze devices. ***EXCEPTION:*** Mix single-constructed devices with separate devices if the combination of devices authorized is not available as a single-constructed device. In this event, place the devices close to one another so they give the appearance of a single-constructed device as long as the devices are the same; i.e., bronze cluster and silver cluster. Wear only separate devices on medals. Wear a maximum of 4 unless wearing more prevents adding a second medal. Wear ribbons awarded by other Services with appropriate device that Service authorized.

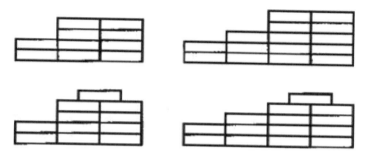

NOTE: VARIATIONS OF RIBBON PLACEMENT WHEN LAPEL OF SERVICE DRESS COAT COVERS PORTIONS OF RIBBONS.

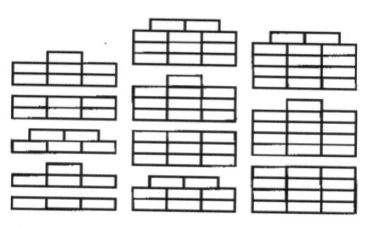

NOTE: VARIATIONS OF RIBBONS WHEN LAPEL OF SERVICE DRESS DOES NOT COVER RIBBONS OR WHEN WEARING RIBBONS ON OTHER SERVICE UNIFORMS.

Arrangement of Medals by Rows, Table 4.1, (see note), (Pgs 130-131)

R	A	B	C	D	E	F	G	H	I	J	K	L
U L E	If number of medals worn is	and the size of medals is	the number of medals in each row is									
			with holding bar				with mounting bar					
			bottom	2d	3d	4th	bottom	2d	3d	4th	5th	6th
1	1 - 5	miniature	1 - 5				1-4	1				
2		regular										
3	6	miniature	6				4	2				
4		regular	3	3								
5	7	miniature	7				4	3				
6		regular	4	3								
7	8	miniature		4			4	4				
8		regular										
9	9	miniature	5				4	4	1			
10		regular										
11	10	miniature		5			4	4	2			
12		regular										
13	11	miniature	6				4	4	3			
14		regular	4	4	3							
15	12	miniature	6	6			4	4	4			
16		regular	4	4	4							
17	13	miniature	7	6			4	4	4	1		
18		regular	5	4	4							
19	14	miniature	7	7			4	4	4	2		
20		regular	5	5	4							
21	15	miniature			5		4	4	4	3		
22		regular										
23	16	miniature	6				4	4	4	4		
24		regular	4	4	4	4						
25	17	miniature	6	6	5		4	4	4	4	1	
26		regular	5	4	4	4						
27	18	miniature	6	6	6		4	4	4	4	2	

R U L E	A	B	C	D	E	F	G	H	I	J	K	L
	If number of medals worn is	and the size of medals is	the number of medals in each row is									
			with holding bar				with mounting bar					
			bottom	2d	3d	4th	bottom	2d	3d	4th	5th	6th
28		regular	5	5	4	4						
29	19	miniature	7	6	6		4	4	4	4	3	
30		regular	5	5	5	4						
31	20	miniature	7	7	6		4	4	4	4	4	
32		regular	5	5	5	5						
33	21	miniature	7	7	7		4	4	4	4	4	1
34	22+	miniature	6	6	6	+	4	4	4	4	4	2

NOTES: (Pg 131)

1. WITH HOLDING BAR: The maximum length of holding bars for medals is 2 3/4 inches. When wearing fewer than 5 miniature medals or 4 regular-size medals, expose all. If wearing more than 4 miniature or 3 regular medals on one row, each medal equally overlaps the medal to the left. The overlap does not exceed 50 percent. Expose the medal nearest the lapel. Stack and center the second or additional row of medals upward. The medal overlaps approximately 50 percent of the ribbon on the row below.

2. WITH MOUNTING BAR: Wear the medal with the highest precedence on the top row nearest the lapel. Stack and center the second and additional rows of medals below. The medal will overlap approximately 50 percent of the ribbon on the row below.

103

Arrangement of Ribbons on Service Uniforms (see notes),
Table 4.2, (Pg 132)

R U L E	A	B		C	D	E
		and the service coat is worn and the lapel			and the size of ribbons worn is	then see notes and wear ribbons in
	If the number of ribbons authorized is	covers portions of the ribbons	does not cover portion of the ribbons			
1	1, 2, 3, or 4			X	regular	a single row.
2	4 thru 8	X				multiples of 3 or 4, centering any remaining ribbons on the top row.
3	4 thru 9			X		
4	7 thru 9	X				multiples of 3 or 4 in 2 bottom rows; but to prevent coat lapel from covering ribbons, each row thereafter may contain less than 3, with top row centered over the row immediately below.
5	10 or more			X		multiples of 3 or 4, with any remaining ribbons centered over the row immediately below.
6	10 or more	X				multiples of 3 or 4 in at least the 2 bottom rows; but to prevent coat lapel from covering ribbons, each additional row may contain less than 3 or 4 or less, with top row centered over the row immediately below.
7	1 thru 6			X	miniature (see note 3)	a single row.
8	1 thru 12			X		multiples of 6 with remaining ribbons centered over the row immediately below.
9	7 or more			X		
10	13 or more			X		multiples of 6 in 2 bottom rows; but to prevent coat lapels from covering ribbons, each additional row may contain less than 6 with the top row centered over the row immediately below.

NOTES: (Pg 133)
1. There is no space between the rows of ribbons.
2. The lapel of the service coat may cover a portion of the ribbons and badges.
3. Women are authorized to wear ribbons in multiples of 4 or 6.

Placement of Medals on Dress Coat or Jacket (see note), Table 4.3, (Pg 133)

R U L E	If the attire is	Then wear miniature medals parallel to the ground on left side of coat or jacket and
1	mess dress jacket	center miniature medals between lapel, and arm seam, and midway between top shoulder seam, and top button of jacket
2	civilian evening dress (men)	align the top of the suspension medal of the top row with (not above) the top of the pocket.
3	civilian black tie	center the holding bar of the bottom row of medals immediately above the pocket; do not wear pocket-handkerchief.

NOTES: (Pg 133)

1. Wear only the regular-size Medal of Honor from the neckband ribbon. Place the ribbon around the neck outside the shirt collar and inside the coat collar. Wear authorized foreign neck decorations beneath the Medal of Honor.

Insignia, Nametags, Badges, and Devices (Pg 134)

Wear of Grade Insignia. Members wear grade insignia as a distinctive part of the uniform. See Table 5.1. Office of Special Investigations (OSI) agents do not wear grade insignia unless AFOSI directs. Chapter 2 of this instruction show proper placement of grade insignia on uniforms.

Wear of the Command Chief Master Sergeant and First Sergeant Insignia. See Table 5.1. Those chief master sergeants assigned to an approved command chief master sergeant authorization and serving in Reporting Identifier 9E000 may wear the command chief master sergeant insignia. Those senior noncommissioned officers assigned to a valid first sergeant authorization serving in Special Duty Identifier 8F000 and have graduated from the USAF First Sergeants Academy, the Air Staff functional manager, and enlisted instructors of the First Sergeant course wear the First Sergeants insignia. Members will remove this special insignia when no longer assigned to command chief master sergeant or first sergeant duties. (Para 5.2, Pg 134)

Nametags. (Para 5.3, Pg 134)

- **Blue Shirt Nametag.** Laminated ultramarine blue plastic material with white, block-style letters engraved on the plastic and a clutch-type fastener. The epoxy nametag is authorized. Make no deviations to the nametag, do not add or change (i.e., emblems, flags, thickness, dimensions, color, etc.) *EXCEPTIONS:* Use smaller letters to fit name within standard tag length and half-size letters if the name has more than 1 capital letter such as MacMANN. Non-physician providers, i.e., physician assistants, obstetrics and gynecological nurse practitioners, pediatric nurse practitioners, primary care nurse practitioners, and independent duty medical technicians (only when performing IDMT duties) wear 2-line nametags to identify their profession. Services personnel wearing organizational uniforms may wear their rank designation on the same line as their last name, i.e., *SSGT BRANCH.* (Para 5.3.1, Pg 134)

- **Service Dress and Pullover Sweater Nametag.** Metal engraved brushed satin finish and blue letters. Make no deviations to the nametag, do not add or change (i.e., emblems, flags, thickness, dimensions, color, etc.) *EXCEPTIONS:* Use smaller letters to fit name within standard tag length and half-size letters if the name has more than 1 capital letter such as MacMANN. Non-physician providers, i.e., physician assistants, obstetrics and gynecological nurse practitioners, pediatric nurse practitioners, primary care nurse practitioners, and independent duty medical technicians (only when performing IDMT duties) wear 2-line nametags to identify their profession. Services personnel wearing organizational uniforms may wear their rank designation on the same line as their last name, i.e., *SSGT BRANCH.* (Para 5.3.2, Pg 134)

USAF/Nametapes. These cloth tapes specify our service, "U.S. Air Force," and the military member's surname. Tape is approximately 6 1/4 inches long and 1 inch wide with 3/4 inch lettering. The "U.S. Air Force" tape is placed over the left pocket, while the nametape is placed over the right pocket. Make no deviations to the USAF/Nametapes. *EXCEPTION:* Use smaller letters to fit name within standard tape length. The tape color will correspond to the particular utility uniform. (Para 5.4, Pg 134)

- Standard Battle Dress Uniform (BDU). Subdued olive green with flag-blue letters embroidered on tape. (Para 5.4.1, Pg 134)
- Desert BDU. Tan in color with brown letters embroidered on tape. (Para 5.4.2, Pg 135)
- Airman Battle Uniform. Tan in color with midnight blue letters embroidered on tape. (Para 5.4.3, Pg 135)

Badges and Specialty Insignia. Table 5.2, Table 5.3, and Table 5.4 show placement and wear instructions for each authorized badge and specialty insignia. See Figure 5.1 for pictures of various badges. (Para 5.5, Pg 135)

Aeronautical and Space Badges. For specific award criteria for Aeronautical Badges, refer to AFI 11-402, *Aviation and Parachutist Service, Aeronautical Ratings and Badges*. For award criteria for the Space Badge, refer to Note 11 of Table 5.2. (Para 5.6, Pg 135)

Duty Badges. Refer to Table 5.3 for a listing of issuing organizations and their duty badges. Duty badges reflect positions of assignment (e.g., Presidential Service Badge). (Para 5.7, Pg 135)

Miscellaneous Badges. Refer to Table 5.2 for a listing of miscellaneous badges authorized to be worn on the uniform. (Para 5.8, Pg 135)

Occupational Badges. Refer to Table 5.4 for a listing of officer and enlisted Air Force Specialty Codes (AFSC) and their occupational badges. Occupational badges are reflective of your AF specialty: (Para 5.9, Pg 135)

- General officers. Wear the basic badge, representative of the organization's mission, upon entering a headquarters staff or command position, unless previously qualified for a higher-level badge. Wear the next higher-level badge after 12 months. Continue to upgrade to next higher level every 12 months. (Para 5.9.1, Pg 135)
- Officers. Wear the basic badge after graduating from technical school (or after attaining a fully qualified AFSC when technical school is not required). Wear the senior badge after 7 years in the specialty and the master badge after 15 years in the specialty. (Para 5.9.2, Pg 135)
  EXCEPTION: Medical Service officers' time in specialty will include any constructive service credit awarded at the time of appointment. Medical Service officers may verify their constructive service credit to determine eligibility for award of badges by contacting HQ AFPC/DPAMF2, 550 C Street West Suite 25, Randolph AFB TX 78150-4727. (Para 5.9.2.1, Pg 135)
- Enlisted. Wear the basic badge after completing technical school. Wear the senior badge after award of the 7-skill level, and the master badge as a master sergeant or above with 5 years in the specialty from award of the 7-skill level.
  EXCEPTION: Air Traffic Controllers (1C1X1) are not authorized to wear the basic badge until facility qualified. (Para 5.9.3, Pg 135)
  EXCEPTION: Chief Master Sergeants who crossflow into a new CEM Code wear the basic badge of their new career field upon award of the CEM Code, the senior badge after 12 months, and the master badge after 5 years. (Para 5.9.3.1, Pg 135)
- Retrainees. Credit toward new badges starts upon entry into new AFSC. (Para 5.9.4, Pg 135)
- Prior enlisted officers. Officers who formerly served as enlisted members may wear the highest awarded occupational badge for the career field in which they served as an enlisted member. When serving as an officer in the same career field as when enlisted, count both time in the enlisted and officer career fields to determine the earned badge level. Time in

Sister Service career fields is not used to determine earned badge level for Air Force occupational badges. (Para 5.9.5, Pg 135)

- When Performing Special Duties or Attending Professional Military Education. Wear primary AFSC occupational badge. Upgrade to the next higher-level badge is awarded in accordance with paragraph 5.9.2 or 5.9.3 respectively. (Para 5.9.6, Pg 136)

Additional Uniform Devices. (Para 5.10, Pg 136)

- Aiguillettes. Aiguillettes distinguish officer aides and attachés. The aide to the President and Vice President of the U.S., White House social aides and aides to foreign heads of state, wear aiguillette on the right; other aides and attachés on the left. See Table 3.6 for eligibility and wear criteria. (Para 5.10.1, Pg 136)
- Commanders' Insignia. See Figure 5.1. The commanders' pin is worn above the nametag on the service dress uniform when in command of a squadron, group, wing, NAF, MAJCOM, or Unified Command. The pin is worn below the nametag upon completion of similar command. Wear on the light blue uniform shirt is similar, above the nametag when in command and below the nametag upon completion of command. (Para 5.10.2, Pg 136)
  - No longer associated with commander's pay. (Para 5.10.2.1, Pg 136)
  - Additional approvals for wear made by CSAF. (Para 5.10.2.2, Pg 136)
  - Maj - Col wear. (Pg 5.10.2.3, Pg 136)
  - Must EXERCISE UCMJ Authority. (Para 5.10.2.4, Pg 136)
  - Must be competitively selected by a board (AFPC/ MAJCOM/FOA, etc). (Para 5.10.2.5, Pg 136)
  - Commanders must be filling: Squadron, Group, or Wing positions. (Para 5.10.2.6, Pg 136)
  - May be worn in the AOR (Per CENTAF, current or prior commanders authorized). (Para 5.10.2.7, Pg 136)

- May not be worn by "temporary" or "acting" commanders. Temporary or Acting commanders may not permanently wear the pin. (Para 5.10.2.8, Pg 136)
- Commanders must serve entire tenure (usually two years) for permanent wear. (Para 5.10.2.9, Pg 136)
- Above the nametag during command; below the nametag post command. (Para 5.10.2.10, Pg 136)
- Vice and Deputy Commanders are not authorized wear of the insignia. However, they may wear the insignia as a graduated commander from previously held command positions. (Para 5.1.2.11, Pg 136)
- Flag Officers are not authorized wear of the insignia. (Para 5.10.2.12, Pg 136)
- Detachment Commanders are not authorized the wear of the commander's insignia. (Para 5.10.2.13, Pg 136)

United States Air Force Officer Ranks	
Service Dress Coat	**Uniform Shirt (Abbreviation)**

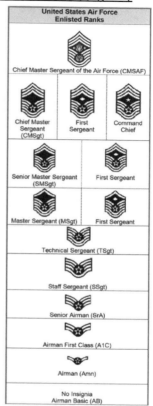

R U L E	A	B	C
	If individual wears the	**And**	**OPR**
1	Chaplain Badge (Mandatory)	if authorized both Chaplain and Aeronautical Badge, wear Chaplain insignia 1/2 inch above aeronautical badge.	HQ USAF/HCX.
2	Air Force Aeronautical and Space badges (Mandatory)	if more than one aeronautical or space badge is worn, wear the badge that reflects current job in the highest position.	HQ USAF/ XOOT.(Aeronautical) (See note 9) HQ USAF/XOS. (Space) (See note 10)
3	Aeronautical badges of other US services (Optional) (See note 10)	if both are worn, wear Air Force aeronautical badge in the highest position.	
4	Air Force Occupational badges (Optional)	if more than one badge is worn, wear badge that reflects current job in the top position.	HQ AFPC/DPSOOC.
Miscellaneous Badges			
5	Combat Infantry, Combat Medical and CAB	only while permanently assigned to and performing duties with other services.	Sister Service Directive - Army MilPERCEN - Navy - BUPERS etc. (See note 11)
6	US Army Air Assault Badge, Pathfinder Badge, Ranger Tab	only while permanently assigned to and performing duties with other services.	Sister Service Directive - Army MilPERCEN - Navy - BUPERS etc. (See note 11)
7	Parachute Riggers Badge	only while permanently assigned to and performing duties with other services.	Sister Service Directive - Army MilPERCEN - Navy - BUPERS etc. (See note 11)
8	Scuba Badge	when awarded.	HQ USAF/XOOS.

NOTES: (Pgs 139-141)

1. A maximum of 4 earned badges may be worn on all blue service uniforms. A maximum of 2 badges are worn on the left side of uniform above ribbons or pocket if ribbons are not worn. Wear only aeronautical, occupational, and miscellaneous badges in this location.

2. Aeronautical and space badges are worn above occupational and miscellaneous badges. When more than 1 aeronautical or space badge is worn, the second badge becomes optional. The parachutist badge is not considered an aeronautical badge, however it does take precedence over other badges.

3. Air Force members are highly encouraged to wear their current occupational badge on all uniform combinations. **A maximum of 2 occupational badges may be worn**. When wearing 2 occupational badges, wear the one representing the current career field (regardless of level earned) in the top position. Centered 1/2 inch above the first one.

4. Men may attach duty badges to service uniforms with a clear plastic tab holder not visible beyond sides or bottom of insignia.

5. A maximum of 3 earned embroidered badges may be worn on all BDUs. A maximum of two badges are worn on the left side of the uniform above the pocket. The third embroidered badge should be worn on the left pocket (such as the Missile badge) or on the right side of the uniform (such as the Commanders Insignia). Wear only aeronautical, occupational and miscellaneous badges in this location.

6. Wear regular size embroidered cloth badges or specialty insignia on the BDU.

7. Mid-size and regular size badges may not be worn together; **EXCEPTION:** Resized wings may be worn with a regular size occupational badge, or regular size medical badge. A regular size duty badge is not worn with a mid-size duty badge.

8. Only highly polished badges are worn. **EXCEPTION:** Oxidized/satin finished "Heritage wings" may be worn. Badges must be all regular or all mid-size.

9. AFI 11-402, *Aviation and Parachutist Service, Aeronautical Ratings and Badges*, for specific award criteria.

10. Guidelines for wear of the Space Badge.

a. The Space Badge is worn by officers and enlisted personnel designated as USAF Credentialed Space Professionals (CSPs).

b. Order of Precedence – The Space Badge is equal in precedence to aeronautical badges and worn above all other occupational badges and the parachutist badge. When awarded both Aeronautical and Space Badges, wear the Space Badge above the Aeronautical Badge only when occupying a space billet. **c.** The criteria to earn the basic, senior and command space badges, respectively, are directly linked to the 3-level Space Professional Certification Program. For enlisted personnel, badge award is not solely linked to skill level attainment. Officer and enlisted personnel may verify their Credentialed Space Professional certification level by contacting the Space Professional Management Office, AFSPC/A1FX, 150 Vandenberg St Suite 1105, Peterson AFB, CO 80914-4450. Call them at DSN 692-3494 or visit their website at: **http://www.peterson.af.mil/spacepro**

d. Basic Space Badge – Certification Level 1 – Completion of Space 100, maintain currency with all acquisition or operational position-specific training requirements, 1 year satisfactory performance in a space-coded billet culminating with Space Professional Certification briefing to Wing CC/CV or equivalent. Additionally, enlisted CSPs must attain the 5 skill level to earn the Basic Space Badge.

e. Senior Space Badge – Certification Level 2 – Completion of Space 200, maintain currency with all position-specific requirements, 6 years satisfactory performance in space-coded billets. **f.** Command Space Badge – Certification Level 3 – Completion of Space 300, maintain currency with all position-specific requirements, 9 years satisfactory performance in space-coded billets. Additionally, enlisted CSPs must complete requirements for CCAF degree in space operations to earn the Command Badge. **g.** CDRUSSTRATCOM and AFSPC/CC are authorized wear of the command Space Badge upon assumption of their position. Not authorized for wear when no longer holding these positions unless it was previously earned. **h.** For General Officers not previously awarded the badge, award the basic Space Badge 1 year after assumption of position and completion of the National Security Space Institute's Space Operations Executive Level Course. Award senior and command badges at one year increments. **i.** AFSPC/CC, as the Space Professional Functional Authority approves qualifying space specialties and award criteria for allied and other U.S. service members. Once the award criteria are approved, allied and other U.S. services will control badge awarding for their respective service members.

11. Permanent assignment denotes non TDY status. This rule also applies to other badges or patches i.e., Army Combat Patches earned or awarded by sister service components. Upon Permanent Change of Station (PCS) to an Air Force unit the member will remove them.

Issuing Organizations and their Duty Badges
Table 5.3, (Pg142-144)

R U L E	A	B	C
	Issuing Organization	**wear**	**OPR**
1	Security Forces	Security Forces Shield while performing duties in control AFSC 31PX or 3P0XX billets only. Continue to wear while attending professional military education and recruiting duties.	HQ USAF/XOF
2	Civil Engineering	Fire Protection Shield while performing duties, professional military education attendance and recruiting duties. Worn by group level personnel and above.	HQ USAF/ILE
3	Defense Commissary Agency	Commissary Badge while performing duties only.	HQ DECA/DO
4	Office of the Secretary of Defense	OSD Badge during and after assignment to the specific duty.	OASD MM&PP
5	Joint Chiefs of Staff	JCS Identification Badge during and after assignment to the specific duty.	JCS/J1
6	Headquarters Air Force Badge	Headquarters Air Force Identification Badge during and after assignment to the specific duty.	AF/A1 (See Note 1)
7	Army Military Personnel Center	Army Staff ID Badge while performing duties only.	Army MILPERCEN
8	North Atlantic Treaty Organization	NATO Badge while performing duties only.	USAFE/A1AP
9	Presidential Service	Presidential Service Badge *or* Vice-Presidential Service Badge during and after an assignment to White House duty.	Military Assistant to the President (See Note 2)
10	United Nations	United Nations Command Badge while performing duties only.	UN
11	Defense Information Systems Agency	DISA Command Badge while performing duties only.	DISA
12	Air Education and Training Command	AETC Instructor Badge while performing assigned duties. Continue to wear while attending professional military education.	HQ AETC/TT

R U L E	A Issuing Organization	B wear	C OPR
		Air Force Recruiting Service Badge while performing assigned duties. Continue to wear while attending professional military education.	HQ AETC/RS
		Air Force Reserve Recruiting Service Badge while performing assigned duties. Continue to wear while attending professional military education.	AFRES/RS
		Jr. ROTC Instructor Badge while performing assigned duties. Continue to wear while attending professional military education.	AFROTC/OT
		Defense Language Instructor Badge while performing assigned duties. Continue to wear while attending professional military education.	DLIFLC
13	Air National Guard	Air National Guard Recruiter Badge while performing assigned duties. Continue to wear while attending professional military education.	ANGCR/ MPPAE
14	Defense Finance and Accoun-ting Service	DFAS Identification Badge while performing duties only.	DFAS
15	Professional Military Education	Professional Military Education Badge while performing PME Instructor or PME Support duties.	AF/A1
16	Military Postal Service	Military Postal Service Identification Badge while performing postal duty.	MPS
17	Defense Logistics Agency	Defense Logistics Agency Command Badge while assigned to DLA only.	DLA
18	USAF Honor Guard and USAF Base Honor Guard	USAF Honor Guard and USAF Base Honor Guard while performing honor guard duties.	HQ USAF/HG
19	Unified Command	Unified Command Identification Badge for the duration of assignment to a Combatant Commander's (COCOM) staff .	Unified COCOM
20	National Defense University	National Defense University Identification Badge while assigned to the NDU faculty or staff.	NDU

R U L E	A Issuing Organization	B wear	C OPR
21	USAF Academy	Permanent Professor USAF Academy Badge during and after assignment to the specific duty.	USAFA

NOTES: (Pg 144)

1. Guidelines for wear of the Headquarters Air Force Badge (as of 22 December 2005)

a. Personnel assigned to Headquarters Air Force and Secretary of the Air Force are authorized to wear the badge. Permanent wear of the badge is authorized for personnel assigned to a qualifying position for at least 365 consecutive days. You are authorized it while you are in the position on the HAF or DRU/FOA within the National Capital Region (NCR).

b. Reserve Members: Members of the Reserve Components are eligible to wear the badge if they are assigned to any organization within Headquarters Air Force or Secretariat Staff. Further, recalled reservists are eligible for permanent award of the badge once they have served for a total of 365 days. Reservists assigned to Individual Mobilization Augmentee positions are eligible for permanent award after being assigned for 1 year and performed satisfactorily in the augmentee position.

c. Order of precedence: The order of precedence for the badge is similar to the OSD or JCS Badges. However, when wearing 3 badges, OSD and JCS badges have priority over the HAF Badge.

d. Wear of the badge is not mandatory. The badge is available in two sizes, large (standard) and a miniature size. The miniature size will be worn on the Air Force Blue Shirt.

2. The Presidential Service identification badge is worn on the **Right** Side. The Vice Presidential Service identification badge is worn on the **Right** Side. No other badges will move the Presidential and Vice-Presidential ID badges.

Occupational Specialties and their Badges (Excludes Aeronautical), Table 5.4, (Pgs 145-147)

	A	B	C
R U L E	Officer Code or Career Field	Enlisted Code or Career Field	Badge Title
Operations Career Group			
1	(S Prefix) Safety Officer (16) Operations Support	(1S, 1T) Safety, Survival Training, Life Aircrew Support, Pararescue	Operations Support
2	None	(1C) Command Control Systems Operations	Command and Control (See note 1.)
	(13B) Air Battle Management	(1C5X1D, 1A4X1D) Weapons Director	Weapons Director (See note 2.)
	(13C) Air Traffic Control Operations	(1C1) Air Traffic Control Operations	Air Traffic Control
3	(13A) Astronaut (13S) Space and Missile Operations	(1C6) Space Systems Operations	Space/Missile (See note 3.)
	(13SXC) Missile Operations	None	Missile with Operations Designator (See note 4.)
4	(14) Intelligence	(1N) Intelligence	Intelligence
5	(15) Weather	(1W) Weather	Meteorologist
Logistics Career Group (See note 5.)			
6	(21A) Aircraft Maintenance and Munitions	(2A, 2P, 2W) Manned Aerospace Maintenance, Precision Measurement, Munitions and Weapons	Maintenance
7	None	(2E) Comm-Electronics Systems	
8	None	(2R) Maintenance Management Systems	
9	(21M) Space and Missile Maintenance	(2M,2W) Missile and Space Systems Maintenance	Missile Maintenance (See note 6.)
		(2W) Munitions and Weapons	
10	(21R) Logistics Readiness Officer	None	Logistics Readiness Officer

	A	B	C
R U L E	**Officer Code or Career Field**	**Enlisted Code or Career Field**	**Badge Title**
11	None	(2S, 2F) Supply, Fuels	Supply/Fuels
12	None	(2T) Transportation	Transportation
13	None	(2G) Logistics Plans	Logistics Plans
14	(32) Civil Engineer	(3E) Civil Engineer	Civil Engineer (See note 7.)
15	(33) Communications and Information	(3C) Comm-Computer Systems	Communications and Information (See note 8.)
16	None	(3A) Information Management	
17	None	(3V) Visual Information	
18	(34) Services	(3M) Services	Services
Support Career Group (See note 5.)			
19	(35B) Band	(3N1) Band	Band
20	(35P) Public Affairs	(3N0) Public Affairs	Public Affairs
21	None	(3H) Historian	Historian
22	(37F) Manpower and Personnel	(3S) Mission Support	Manpower and Personnel (See note 9.)
Support/Investigations Career Groups			
23	(31) Security Forces	(3P) Security Forces/CATM/ MWD	Force Protection
24	(71) Special Investigations	(7S) Special Investigations	
Professional Career Group			
25	(51) Judge Advocate	None	Judge Advocate
26	(52) Chaplain	None	Chaplain
27	None	(5J) Paralegal	Paralegal
28	None	(5R) Chaplain Service Support	Chaplain Service Support
29	(61, 62) Scientific/ Research, Developmental Engineering	None	Acquisition and Financial Management
30	(63) Acquisition		
31	(64) Contracting	(6C) Contracting	

	A	B	C
R U L E	**Officer Code or Career Field**	**Enlisted Code or Career Field**	**Badge Title**
Acquisition and Financial Management Career Group			
32	(65) Financial Management	(6F) Financial Management	
Medical Career Group			
33	(40) (44) (45) (48) Physician (MC)	None	Medical Corps
34	(41) Health Service Administrator (MSC)	None	Medical Service Corps
35	(42) (43) Biomedical Science Officer (BSC)	None	Biomedical Science Corps
36	(46) Nurse Corps (NC)	None	Nurse Corps
37	(47) Dentist (DC)	None	Dental Corps
38	None	(4XXXX) Enlisted Medical Service Member	Enlisted Medical

NOTES: (Pgs 147-148)

1. If both the Command and Control badge and Weapons Director badge are earned, subsequent levels can be earned toward 1 badge only.

2. If both Air Battle Manager Wings and the Weapons Director badge are earned, subsequent levels can only be earned on the Air Battle Manager Wings.

3. The old Space/Missile Badge is authorized for former space-experienced officers and enlisted space personnel who earned the badge, but permanently retrained to a new AFSC prior to 1 Nov 05. This includes a variety of AFSCs (e.g., 18XX, 20XX, 27XX, 28XX, 277XX, 207XX, 13SXX, 6XXXX, 1C6XX, 1NXXX, etc.) that were awarded the old Space/Missile Badge via AF Form 117. This badge is authorized for wear until the individuals separate or retire. These personnel are not entitled to wear the Space Badge instituted on 1 Nov 05.

4. The Missile Badge with Operations Designator is authorized for former 13SXX officers who served in missile operations, but permanently retrained to a new core AFSC prior to 1 Nov 05. This badge is authorized for wear until personnel separate or retire.

These personnel are not authorized to wear the Space Badge instituted on 1 Nov 05.

5. Officers in AFSC 20, Logistics Commander, and AFSC 30, Support Commander, wear the highest badge the individual was awarded in the Logistics or Support career areas. If the individual was not awarded a Logistics or Support badge, wear the highest badge they were awarded from the previous career area.

6. To qualify for the Missile Maintenance badge, individuals must meet all criteria outlined in paragraph 5.9 and meet time requirements in their entirety, to include the following:

a. Munitions and Missile Maintenance Officers who do not attend Missile Maintenance Officers course, must directly supervise 2M/2W personnel in maintenance, loading or unloading of guided missiles or missile systems for a period of 12 months after completion of Munitions Maintenance Officers course in order to wear the basic badge. Subsequent levels will be IAW paragraph 5.9.

b. 2W personnel must directly work with guided missiles or missile systems for a period of 12 months after completion of technical training school in order to wear the basic badge. Subsequent levels will be IAW paragraph 5.9.**7.** Explosive Ordnance Disposal (EOD) and Readiness will wear their specific duty badges in addition to the CE Craftsmen Badge.

8. Officers in former AFSCs 13BXF (Adjutants), 33SX (Communications-Computers), 33VX (Visual Information), and 37AX (Information Management), integrated into the communications and Information career field, wear the Communications and Information Badge and maintain the same level (basic, senior, master) as worn on previous 13BXF, 33SX, 33VX, and 37AX occupational badges. However, effective 1 Nov 96, stars and wreaths are "earned" on the new Communications and Information badge only.

9. Effective 1 Oct 05, officers in AFSCs 36XX Mission Support; Personnel and 38XX Manpower were integrated into a combined AFSC 37FX Manpower and Personnel career field. Officers previously in the AFSCs 36XX and 38XX may use that accrued time to upgrade to the next higher-level badge in accordance with paragraph 5.9. Additionally, officers in the former Information

Management career field (AFSC 37XX), who crossflowed into
AFSC 36XX prior to 1 Nov 96, may use that accrued time to
upgrade to the next higher-level badge in accordance with
paragraph 5.9.

Display of Badges, Figure 5.1. (Pgs 149-150)

Acquisition & Financial Manager	Air Traffic Control	Astronaut	Band
Biomedical Science Corps	Buddhist Chaplain	Chaplain Service Support	Civil Engineer Readiness
Christian Chaplain	Civil Engineer	Command & Control	Commander
Communications & Information	Dental Corps	Enlisted Aircrew	Enlisted Medical
Explosive Ordnance Disposal	Fire Fighter	Flight Nurse	Flight Surgeon
Force Protection	Historian	Information Management	Intelligence
Jewish Chaplain	Judge Advocate	Logistics Plans	Logistics Readiness Officer
Maintenance	Manpower & Personnel	Medical Corps	Medical Services Corps
Meteorologist	Missile	Missile with Ops Designator	Muslim Chaplain
Navigator/Observer	Nurse Corps	Officer Aircrew Member	Operations Support
Parachutist	Paralegal	Pilot	Public Affairs
Security Forces	Services	Space	Space/Missile
Supply Fuels	Transportation	Weapons Director	

R U L E	A If the member is	B may wear the uniform	C and is authorized to wear the appropriate uniforms
1	in any of the categories	when traveling to and from any function listed in this table, when travel in uniform is within 24 hours of the scheduled function.	according to the rules below.
2		at any time, when he or she has been awarded the Medal of Honor and **Chapter 1** does not prohibit wear of the uniform.	
3	a reservist (on active duty)	when participating in short periods of active duty (including active duty for training)	listed in this instruction.
4	a reservist not on EAD and residing in the US, its territories, or possessions	when participating in authorized inactive duty training, unit training assemblies, or equivalent training	
5		when engaged in military flying activities, including traveling as a passenger on military aircraft	
6		on occasions of military ceremony	
7		social functions and informal gatherings of a military nature	
8		when engaged in military instruction	

R U L E	A If the member is	B may wear the uniform	C and is authorized to wear the appropriate uniforms
9		when responsible for military discipline at an educational institution	listed in this instruction.
10	a reservist not on EAD and not residing in the US, its territories, or possessions	when authority is granted by the Secretary of the Air Force	
11		at military ceremonies or other functions of a military nature, provided authority is granted; such authority may be obtained by reporting to the nearest military attaché	
12	an airman with Air Force Reserve commission	of his or her Reserve grade when attending meetings or functions of associations formed for military purposes (membership will be mostly officers or former officers)	
13	an ANG technician	according to ANG regulations while performing air technician duties, however, they do not receive a uniform allowance for voluntarily wearing the uniform (see notes 2 - 5)	
14	an Air Reserve technician	must when performing duty in civil service status as an Air Reserve Technician	
15	an Air Reserve technician	DELETED	
16	retired	at occasions of military ceremonies	prescribed at date of retirement, or any of the uniforms authorized for active duty personnel, including the dress uniforms. Do not mix uniform items (see notes 6 and 7).

R U L E	A If the member is	B may wear the uniform	C and is authorized to wear the appropriate uniforms
17		military funerals, weddings, memorial services, and inaugurals	
18		patriotic parades on national holidays, other military parades or ceremonies in which any active or Reserve US military unit is taking part	
19		at educational institutions when engaged in giving military instructions or responsible for military discipline	
20		at social or other functions when the invitation has been influenced by the member's active military service	
21	separated (other than retired ANG or Reserve) (war service)	at military funerals, memorial services, and inaugurals	authorized at time of separation or any of the uniforms authorized for active duty personnel if they served honorably in the Air Force (including service with an air component of the Army before the Air Force was established), during a declared or undeclared war (see notes 8 and 9).
22		patriotic parades on national holidays; military parades or ceremonies in which any active or Reserve US military unit is taking part	
23		on any other occasion when authorized by law	
24	separated (other than retired, ANG, or Reserve) (non war service)	from place of discharge to home, within 3 months after discharge	of the highest grade authorized at time of separation (see note 9).

1. Members will conform to the same standards of appearance, military customs, practices, and conduct in uniform prescribed for active duty members.

2. Title 10, U.S.C., Section 772 entitles members of the ANG to wear the uniform as prescribed for active duty members.

3. State-appointed ANG officers without federal recognition do not wear the uniform or any distinctive uniform item. Newly appointed ANG officers granted temporary federal recognition by a federal recognition board wear the uniform.

4. Enlisted ANG members wear the uniform on enlistment.

5. Upon written request of the governor and the consent of the Air Force Chief of Staff, the Chief of the National Guard Bureau authorizes a state adjutant general, who holds a federally commissioned status in the Air Force, to wear the grade insignia of his or her state-appointed grade while occupying the federally recognized position on the state headquarters unit manning documents, provided that grade does not exceed Major General.

6. Members receive the retired lapel button at retirement. Retirees wear the retired lapel button on the left lapel. Members whose assignments have included command at squadron, group, or wing level are also authorized to wear the command insignia pin on the left lapel, below the retired lapel button.

7. Members whose last assignment prior to retirement was a First Sergeant and/or Command Chief may wear appropriate chevrons in all instances the uniform is worn.

8. Retirees may wear civilian clothing when flying in military aircraft. They will present a favorable appearance in good taste. Members of the reserve components who are eligible to retire but are not at mandatory retirement age (60 years) do not wear the uniform while traveling on military aircraft.

9. Honorably discharged members who served during World War II wear the Honorable Discharge Emblem on the left lapel.

10. Installation commanders authorize such separatees to use military clothing sales stores (MCSS) to purchase uniforms and accessories required for special occasions such as military funerals, parades, or other ceremonies. Separatees purchase only the service dress or mess dress uniforms and accessories. Separatees may not purchase items commonly available from commercial sources. MCSSs establish adequate controls over quantities of uniform items each separatee purchases. Commanders ensure separatees present proof of honorable discharge under honorable conditions and know current uniform and grooming standards.

<u>***Uniform Changes and Supplements***</u>
<u>***(Pgs 156-157)***</u>

How To Recommend Uniform Changes. Submit proposals for new or changed uniform clothing items and wear criteria into the Air Force IDEA Program Data System (IPDS [**https://ideas.randolph.af.mil**]). Process applications in accordance with AFI 38-401, *The Air Force Innovative Development Through Employee Awareness (IDEA) Program.* Process requests for reconsideration for disapproved proposals the same as initial proposals. They are exempt from the automatic higher-level review provisions of AFI 38-401. (Para 7.1, Pg 156)

• Processing IDEAs. Host base MPF Customer Service Element considers each proposal. Base-level agencies, e.g., hospital, and safety, provide comments as needed. The installation commander signs proposals recommended for approval with rationale for approval and forwards to the submitter's MAJCOM Director of Personnel. The MPF Commander has disapproval authority when the proposal is not a new idea, when it duplicates a previous idea with "ownership" rights, or when the proposal clearly is not beneficial or desirable. The MPF Commander will complete the evaluation in IPDS as the disapproving authority and will include the reason for the disapproval. For disapproval reasons other than above, the MPF Commander will include the following statement in the text of the evaluation "not recommended for adoption, but

disapproval not within the authority of this office"
(Para 7.1.1, Pg 156)

- Uniform Boards. Uniform Boards. MAJCOMs conduct their own uniform boards to evaluate each proposal. The commander, vice commander, or chief of staff signs proposals recommended for approval and sends them to HQ AFPC/DPSOOC, 550 C Street West, Suite 37, Randolph AFB TX 78150-4738. HQ AFPC/ DPSOOC will conduct a quality review and consolidate proposals to the Air Force Uniform Board (AFUB). The AFUB evaluates each proposal and makes recommendations to the Chief of Staff, USAF. If the MAJCOM disapproves the proposal, return it and the reasons for disapproval through command channels.
(Para 7.1.2, Pg 156)

- Air Staff, Field Operating Agencies (FOA), and Direct Reporting Units (DRU) Recommendations. FOA and DRU commanders, Air Staff Deputy Chiefs of Staff (DCS), and their assistants, submit recommendations directly to the AFUB. (Para 7.1.3, Pg 156)

- Air Force Academy Uniform Board. The Superintendent, United States Air Force Academy (USAFA), appoints an Air Force Academy Cadet Uniform Board to review all proposed changes to Air Force cadet and preparatory school student uniforms. The Superintendent may approve changes regarding USAFA cadet and preparatory student uniform accessories and insignia, but must send other proposed changes to the Chief of Staff, USAF, for final approval. Proposed changes to the standard Air Force uniform or wear criteria are submitted directly to the AFUB. (Para 7.1.4, Pg 156)

- The AFUB. This board, composed of senior Air Force personnel, ensures the Air Force uniform is plain and distinctive, and develops consistent policy on all uniform matters. It reviews and selects items of uniform clothing, accessories, and insignia, which the Chief of Staff, AF, approves. AFUB changes are effective when incorporated into this instruction or other guidance as prescribed by AF/A1. (Para 7.1.5, Pg 156)

- Test Uniforms. Members wear test uniform items as part of an authorized test program. Unless, otherwise directed, members may wear test uniform items approved for Air Force use after the test period. AF/A1 determines which individuals, units or commands will test new uniform items. (Para 7.1.6, Pg 156)

Processing Supplements. (Para 7.2, Pg 157)
- Include all rules for local wear and additional uniform guidance in a supplement to this directive. Refer to AFI 33-360, Vol 1, *Air Force Content Management Program-- Publications*. (Para 7.2.1, Pg 157)
- MAJCOMs approve their base supplements if instructions are within the guidelines of the basic directive. Coordinate any proposals deviating from current policy with Headquarters Air Force Personnel Center, Current Operations Branch, (HQ AFPC/ DPSOOC), 550 C Street West, Suite 37, Randolph Air Force Base, TX 78150-4737 before incorporating them into the supplement. DPSOOC approves all MAJCOM and FOA supplements. Ensures all are consistent with this instruction. Upon publication, send one copy and any changes to DPSOOC. (Para 7.2.2, Pg 157)
- Proposed ANG unit supplements are submitted through the state Adjutant General to the Air National Guard Readiness Center, NGB/DPF- FOC, for approval. Each unit sends a copy of its approved published supplement and changes to the appropriate Adjutant General and Air National Guard Bureau Readiness Center, Director for Personnel, upon publication. (Para 7.2.3, Pg 157)

Fourrageres and Lanyards	1 Jan 1993
White Ceremonial Dress Uniform	1 Mar 1993
Two-line Nametags	31 Oct 1993
Blue Ceremonial Dress Uniform	1 Aug 1994
Blue Beret	30 Sep 1994
Maternity Smock	30 Sep 1994
Blue Formal Dress Headgear	30 Sep 1994
Olive Green T-shirts	1 Oct 1994
Satin/oxidized U.S. insignia	1 Jun 1995
U.S. Insignia With Circle	1 Jun 1995
Service Dress Coat, Shade 1549	30 Sep 1996
Officers Service Dress Coat, Shade 1620 with Officer Sleeve Rank and no Epaulets	30 Sep 1996
Long and Short-Sleeved Blouse With Fly-Front Closure With Rounded Collar	1 Jan 1997
OG 107/507 Field Jacket	1 Jan 1997
Embroidered Badges and Specialty Insignia Worn on Dress Uniform Combinations	1 Oct 1997
BDU Aircrew Style Name Patch	1 Oct 1997
Women's Service Dress Hat (Blue and White)	1 Oct 1997
Men's and Women's Single-Breasted All Weather Coat	1 Mar 1998
Satin and Oxidized finish Belt Tip and Buckle	1 Oct 1998
Satin and Oxidized Finish Badges and Specialty Insignia, Regular and Miniature	1 Oct 1998
Service Dress Coat, Shade 1598 (Polyester Double-Knit)	30 Sep 1999
Service Dress Coat, Shade 1608 (Polyester Wool Tropical)	30 Sep 1999
Women's Ruffled Mess Dress Blouse	1 Jan 2000
Circles will be worn around the U.S. Insignias.	1 Jan 2007

NCO's will no longer wear shoulder boards on   1 Aug 2006
their blue shirts. Shoulder boards will only be
worn by SNCO's on the blue cardigan sweater.
Junior NCO's and Airmen will continue to use the
in on rank.

Gray Scarf   31 Dec 2010

Maternity Service Dress Coat, Scarves, Gloves, Mittens, Earmuffs
(Gray and Dark Blue) (5 years out)

RIBBONS

In Order of Precedence

MOH	AFC	DDSM	DSM	SSM	DSSM
LOM	DFC	AmnM	BSM	PH	DMSM
MSM	AM	AAM	JSCM	AFCM	JSAM
AFAM	AFCAM	AF PUC	GUC	JMUA	MUA
AFOUA	AFOEA	POWM	CRM	AFCGM	GCM
ARFMSM	OAYR	AFRR	ADSM	ACM	APCM
EAMECM	WWII VM	AOM	MHA	NDSM	KSM
ASM	AFEM	VSM	SWASM	KCM	AfgCM
ICM	GWOT-E	GWOT-S	KDSM	AFSM	HSM
MOVSM	ASCM	AFOR-ST	AFOR-LT	AFESR	AFLSA
AFBMTIR	AFRecR	AFResM	NCOPMEGR	BMTHGR	SAEMR
AFTR	Phil DM	Phil LM	Phil IM	Phil PUC	Kor PUC
RVNGCwP	UNSM	UNM	NATO MSM	NATO MYug	NATO MKos
Art5 NATO Eagle Assist	Art5 NATO Active End	Non Art5 NATO Balk	Non Art5 ISAF	RVCM	KLM-Saudi
KLM-Kuwait	RK-KWSM				